Photo: Tony Lewis

Sean Riley was born in Burnie, Tasmania, in 1967 and spent most of his childhood dreaming of escape. He got his wish in 1989, when he moved to Adelaide, taking Oddbodies, the theatre company he co-founded with Kim Liotta, with him. His recent writing credits include *The Time of Ashes* (Urban Myth Theatre of Youth, UMTOY for Come Out 01); *The Last Acre* (Oddbodies, 2003); *Significant Others* (Oddbodies, 2005); *My Sister Violet* (UMTOY, 2005); *The Sad Ballad of Penny Dreadful* (Windmill Performing Arts and Mainstreet Theatre, 2006); *Beautiful Words* (Oddbodies, 2006); and *The Angel and The Priest* (Oddbodies as part of the Adelaide Festival, 2008).

His play *Significant Others* was short-listed for the Patrick White Playwright Award, and *Beautiful Words* won the Adelaide Theatre Guide's Curtain Call Award for Best Dramatic Production of the 2005/06 season; the Adelaide Theatre Critic's 2006 Ozcart Award for Best New Play; the 2004 Jill Blewett Playwright's Award; was nominated for a 2007 AWGIE for Best Play for Young Audiences and short-listed for the 2004 Patrick White Playwright's Award. *The Angel and the Priest* received an Honorable Mention for the RAI Prix Italia's award for original work and was broadcast as a radio play on ABC Radio National.

A 2004 recipient of an Australia Council Literature Board Established Writers New Work Grant and the 2005 Arts SA Established Artist Fellowship, Sean is currently writing and developing several projects, including *The Poisoned Wife*, a feature-length screenplay set in 1850s Tasmania.

Kim Liotta (left) as Pearl and Jacqy Phillips as Lurl from the 2006 Oddbodies Theatre Company production in Adelaide. Part 2: Pantheon. (Photo: Tony Lewis)

Beautiful Words

Sean Riley

Currency Press, Sydney

CURRENCY TEENAGE SERIES

First published in 2008
by Currency Press Pty Ltd,
PO Box 2287, Strawberry Hills, NSW, 2012, Australia.
enquiries@currency.com.au
www.currency.com.au

Reprinted 2014

NATIONAL LIBRARY OF AUSTRALIA CIP DATA

Author:	Riley, Sean, 1967–.
Title:	Beautiful words / author, Sean Riley.
Publisher:	Strawberry Hills, N.S.W.: Currency Press, 2008.
ISBN:	9780868198323 (pbk.)
Dewey Number:	A822.4

Typeset for Currency Press by Dean Nottle.
Printed by Lightning Source.
Cover design by Laura McLean, Currency Press.
Front cover shows Andreas Sobik as Papa and Eliza Lovell as Mama from Part One: Zugang; back cover shows Tim Morgan as Ari and Eliza Lovell as his Mother, from Part Three: Epiphany. Both photographs from the 2006 Oddbodies production. (Photography: Tony Lewis)

Contents

Introduction

Beautiful Words, Harsh Realities and Somewhere Over the Rainbow

Murray Bramwell

In December 2001 a story was published in the *Age* newspaper about a young Afghan girl named Zaynab. Her photo shows a very typical looking 12-year-old wearing a boldly patterned headscarf—but, unlike most 12-year-olds, her expression is solemn, her eyes downcast. The report notes that although she is in the care of her uncle, a government spokesman says her future in Australia is uncertain.

Zaynab was one of only four children who survived the sinking of the infamous SIEV-X, a boat containing more than 400 refugees from Afghanistan via Jakarta, which capsized in international waters causing 65 men, 142 women and 146 children to drown. From Zaynab's immediate family her mother, father and four siblings all lost their lives. Her six-year-old brother Mahmoud died beside her, as the report says, 'choking on a deadly cocktail of fuel and seawater'.[1]

This article, says Sean Riley, was one of the triggers for his play for young people, *Beautiful Words*, written and developed over four years from late 2001. During that time a number of maritime emergencies occurred in addition to SIEV-X. There was also the Tampa crisis in August 2001 and the infamous 'children overboard' incident just days prior to the December 2001 Federal Election.

'There was a whole lot of turmoil and press about children overboard,' Riley recalls, 'and it seriously took my breath away, this clinical, detached approach to children. How could the government provide so little certainty for a child? And as I worked on the play I was able to observe how the world was changing, how borders were changing and how politics and public opinion were altering.'[2]

Much has been written documenting the politicisation of asylum seekers—the hardline policies against illegal immigrants, the use of

---

[1] Kelly Burke, 'Orphaned survivor faces uncertain future', *Sydney Morning Herald*, Dec 21, 2001.

[2] Personal interview with Sean Riley, Adelaide, 26 March, 2008. All subsequent quotes are from this conversation.

the navy to turn boats away, the expansion of detention centres on the Australian mainland and the establishment (known as the Pacific Solution) of detention centres on outlying islands such as Nauru.[3] The slow processes of refugee verification, the arduous internment, including that of families and children, and the issuing of temporary visas created a climate of anxiety, uncertainty and despair. Some asylum seekers in custody resorted to violence and self-harm, sewing their lips together in silent protest and refusing food and medication.

These events formed a continuing narrative in the first years of the twenty-first century, amplified by the fear and mistrust of the Middle East and the Muslim religion after the attacks on New York and Washington on September 11, 2001. Australian society was divided about these questions. It became a major feature of political campaigns. In the lead-up to the election in November 2001 a defiant Prime Minister John Howard announced: 'We decide who comes to this country and the circumstances in which they come'. Many Australians strongly supported punitive government action and policies, while others wrote letters of protest and formed support groups to assist refugees who were forbidden to work, yet expected to manage without support from the authorities.

These turbulent events form the background to *Beautiful Words* but they are not the subject of Sean Riley's play. When the Afghan boy, Ari, is miraculously washed up at Herring Bay in North Western Australia, it conjures up these recent occurrences—leaky boats, illegal entry, misery and death on the high sea—but the play is preoccupied with more personal imaginings and a larger timeframe also.

The contemporary events in the play are part of a larger wheel of history which goes back to 1945. In the first of its three sections, entitled *Zugang* (meaning 'access' in German), Riley begins his story in the Auschwitz Birkenau Camp in Poland in 1945, during the last weeks of the World War II and prior to Germany's surrender to the Allies.

Here the young gypsy boy, Roman Kansler, forms an unlikely, but very natural friendship with a German boy, Jan Klein-Rogge. They are

---

[3] Some relevant further reading includes: Marr, David and Marian Wilkinson, *Dark Victory*, Allen and Unwin, 2004. Peter Mares, *Borderline: Australia's Treatment of Refugees and Asylum Seekers in the Wake of the Tampa*, New South Wales University Press, 2003. Robert Manne with David Corlett, 'Sending Them Home: Refugees and the New Politics of Indifference', *Quarterly Essay* Issue 13, 2004.

in a terrible place, one interned, the other a child of the jailers. But they are also just boys who love to hang out together and go skating, doing normal things in a cruelly insane environment. Jan learns how myths are devised to justify fears—slanderous stories about Jews and Gypsies, providing reasons to exclude and dominate. But his own experience also contradicts that. When he meets a Gypsy close up, and becomes friends with him, the stereotypes explode, the prejudice fades.

Something very similar happens in Part 2, *Pantheon*, named for the magical movie house run by the zany Pearl and Lurline up at Herring Bay. When Ari arrives he is a strange and frightened figure. The impulse of those who find him is to offer kindness and sanctuary. But there is also apprehension and suspicion as exhibited by Sheree, who not only runs the post office but is the self-appointed border protection monitor. For her, issues are black and white and the power of exclusion is an important part of her sense of her own belonging. We learn that she was not always Sheree, but was once called Ottla Pavlukovic. She carries painful memories as a recently arrived migrant herself, of being ridiculed for eating salami and called racist names. Her situation reminds us that, apart from the first inhabitants, everyone is a boat person, that Australian history is a succession of arrivals from somewhere else.

It could be said that *Beautiful Words* is about the suspicion that we have for 'other' people. We love our own kind of clannish loyalty, but often fear and despise those who are strange or different. Until, of course, we get to know them, then preconceptions and abstract hatreds tend to fall away.

Not only is this Riley's theme, it also his strategy. As his audience we are encouraged to recognise familiar bonds with the young Ari as he hides out at the Pantheon watching old movies. As he learns English from the beautiful words of the cinema, we share the pizazz of Gene Kelly and Judy Garland, the romance of *Casablanca*, the dark intensity of Cagney and Garbo, and those powerful stories of home and the separation from it: Dorothy in the *Wizard of Oz* and the forlorn ET, pining to phone home. As Ari soaks up this popular culture, his emotions and aspirations are no different from ours, and just as familiar as Zaynab, the young SIEV-X survivor in the newspaper article, whose one wish was to learn English and study to be a doctor.

The migration stories in *Beautiful Words* cross several generations and deal with both simple and complex truths. As Riley observes of those citizens close to the terrible events in the camps: 'I don't think everyone who was there believed in what they were doing'. If atrocities occur when good people do nothing, then small positive actions have large meanings. When Jan takes on the identity of his friend Roman, he is also doing penance and redeeming his shame for his family. When Saul Greenberg appears in Part 3, he is the international voice for refugees and he is also speaking out in a way that few did when his own mother was interned and narrowly escaped death in the camp.

Sean Riley is careful not to draw comparisons between current events and the Holocaust. He states that: 'In some ways I wanted to put things into rational comparison, to make clear that the Holocaust and asylum seeker issues are quite different. I wanted to debunk that myth—but also to show what happens when people stand aside and do nothing'.

Beautiful Words takes us in large sweeps from Europe to Afghanistan to various parts of Australia. But the connections are always precise and poignantly human ones. Sean Riley has said he wanted to find a way to express big questions with a young voice, one that will speak directly, and not down, to school-age audiences. And so he does with young Jan and Roman, Ari and Trent, and later, Ari and Toby. In the familiarity of their larking about, in the natural alliances they form—all other divisions, German and Gypsy, Afghan and backblocks Australian, dissolve. As they do with the older generations: Stella, the bitter widow of a Vietnam veteran is suspicious of her Muslim neighbour until a hospital emergency brings them together and barriers are broken down. Named for the young girl in the newspaper article which was one of the triggers for the play, the bonds the young refugee mother Zaynab form with her fellow Australian are both credible and hopeful.

Beautiful Words is a play of symmetries and magical coincidences, tribulations and strongly affirmative resolution. In vibrant, strongly theatrical ways—with music in Part 1, giddy comedy of Pearl and Lurl and their tinsel Pantheon in Part 2, and in the vivid scenes of connection in Part 3, Riley has created the credible conditions for reconciliation and understanding. In the memorable scene between Old Roman and Mrs Greenberg, rolling lemons under their toes to relieve their tired feet, a simple but powerful visual metaphor is established which typifies the play's instinctive humanity. The title refers to the enticing, but deceptive words, of dictators, but it also refers to the hopeful lyrics of cinema musicals and the new words of a new language, experienced for the first time.

Sean Riley has said that he wanted *Beautiful Words* to be an epic play for young people 'that challenged them about the world we live in. It came from speaking to my young friends about the concerns they have about migration, the Eastern world, the battle between Christian and Muslim. And it is asking, sympathetically and without fear, if you had to leave your own country, would you want, would you expect, to be accepted somewhere else?'

Adelaide
April 2008

Murray Bramwell is Associate Professor in Drama at Flinders University in Adelaide, South Australia. He is also a theatre reviewer for the *Australian* and *Adelaide Review.*

This play is dedicated to the memory of my nephew
Thomas Ian McLeod (1988 - 2005).

First Production

Beautiful Words was first produced by Oddbodies Theatre Company, at Higher Ground, Adelaide, on 5 May 2006, with the following cast:

Kapo / Harry / Uncle Ramal	Craig Behenna
Mrs Damrosch / Pearl / Stella	Kim Liotta
Mama / Sheree / Ari's Mother / Helen / Zaynab	Eliza Lovell
Young Roman / Ari	Tim Morgan
Old Roman / Alf	Dennis Olsen
Toby / Jan / Trent	Gabriel Partington
Viorica / Lurline / Mrs Greenberg	Jacqy Phillips
Ion / Saul	Stephen Sheehan
Papa / Victor / Ari's Father / Technician	Andreas Sobik

Director, Sean Riley
Designer, Dean Hills
Lighting Designer, Sue Grey-Gardner
Sound Designer, Angus MacDonald

Tim Morgan (left) as Roman and Gabriel Partington as Jan in the 2006 Oddbodies Theatre Company production in Adelaide. Part 1: Zugang. (Photo: Tony Lewis)

Part 1:
Zugang

Characters

Actor 1:	**Old Roman**, late 60s
Actor 2:	**Toby / Jan**, both 14
Actor 3:	**Mama**, early 40s
Actor 4:	**Papa**, early 40s
Actor 5:	**Mrs Damrosch**, early 50s
Actor 6:	**Viorica**, early 60s
Actor 7:	**Young Roman**, 15
Actor 8:	**Ion**, 40s
Actor 9:	**Kapo**, late 30s

Setting

The action moves between:

The present, a park in Australia; and
1945, Auschwitz Birkenau concentration camp in Poland.

Scene One

A park. Night.

OLD ROMAN sits on a park bench at the edge of the space. He sings 'Keserves', a Hungarian lament, quietly.

TOBY skates around the space. He halts, a moment before OLD ROMAN stops singing.

Old Roman I don't know the rest.

Toby [*to the audience*] My grandfather sings in many languages, but speaks in only one. English. He was born somewhere in Europe, and came to this country when he was eighteen.

Old Roman How does it end?

Toby I don't know. [*To the audience*] What happened between birth and Australia is a no-go zone. He's never talked about it. That time. To anyone.

Old Roman [*to himself*] Something about a bird... in a cage...

Toby [*to the audience*] There are no photos. No memories. No friends.

Old Roman [*to himself*] And something about a letter arriving... I'm a stupid old man...

> *He pulls up his sleeve and stares at his arm.*

Toby [*to the audience*] My grandfather has a tattoo on his arm. But it isn't a pretty thing. It's an ugly black number. B3606. The B stands for Birkenau, a section of Auschwitz concentration camp in Poland, during World War Two. It was a horrible place. It's the reason he never talks about his past. And why we never ask.

Old Roman How does it end...? [*He rolls down his sleeve.*] You got chocolate?

> *TOBY gives him a chocolate bar. OLD ROMAN scoffs it.*

Toby Jeez, Granddad—it's freezing. I don't know why we come here. People usually go to the park in the daytime. In summer.

Old Roman Stop your grizzling. You don't know what cold is. Besides, the stars are pretty.

TOBY watches him scoff the chocolate.

Toby I know why you like chocolate so much.

Old Roman Do you?

Toby Uh-huh. 'Cause you didn't have any when you were a kid. In the war.

Old Roman In war no one has anything. Especially chocolate.

Toby But where you were. It was worse. The camp.

Old Roman Why do you keep doing this? Asking these questions? Why the sudden interest?

Toby Because I want to know, Granddad.

Old Roman It's best forgotten.

Toby Lots of others don't think so. Other survivors. People like you.

Old Roman They are not like me. I am not like them.

Toby They have museums now.

Old Roman There are things… people… that should be left in peace.

Toby Why can't you tell me? I can handle it.

Old Roman *Enough!*

> *The lights change.*
>
> *YOUNG ROMAN, a memory, enters and stands some distance away, and sings 'Keserves'.*
>
> *OLD ROMAN stares at him and points.*

Toby What is it, Granddad?

Old Roman Him.

Toby Who?

Old Roman [*pointing*] Him!

Toby I can't see anyone.

Old Roman Can't you hear him singing?

Toby Who?

> *The song ceases.*
>
> *YOUNG ROMAN fades into the darkness.*

Old Roman [*standing, to YOUNG ROMAN*] No! Don't leave me!

Toby Granddad!?

Old Roman [*to YOUNG ROMAN*] Tell me how it ends!

Toby Who are you talking to?

> *OLD ROMAN stares silently at TOBY.*

Why can't you tell me? I only want to know because I love you.
I deserve to know. Before you forget. Before you're not here
anymore.

> *Silence.*
>
> *TOBY's mood turns.*

I'm tired of living with your ghosts. And I'm tired of the silence.
And so is Mum. Why don't you tell me. Huh?

> *TOBY gives up and wanders away.*

Old Roman [*making an effort*] It's a boy. A boy I remember. From the
camp. His name was Roman. Roman Kansler.

Toby [*halting*] That's your name, Granddad.

Old Roman He was a fine boy. Strong. Proud. A gypsy boy... And
there was another boy. Jan. Jan Klein-Rogge. A German boy,
whose father worked at the camp... He was sickly, weak, lonely.
But wilful. Far too big for his boots... They were so different.
These two boys. From opposite sides of the wall. For them, a
friendship was impossible. But sometimes... magic happens...
even in the darkest of places.

> *A train bellows in the distance.*
>
> *The lights change.*

Scene Two

*The German side of the wall. A courtyard at the edge of Birkenau
concentration camp. Winter, 1945. Night-time.*

Light spills from a house.

*YOUNG ROMAN stands inside the gate. He is carrying a heavy sack. He
walks closer, staring into the house.*

MRS DAMROSCH, a servant, enters.

Mrs Damrosch What are you doing here?

Young Roman Coal. For their fire.

Mrs Damrosch Then leave it, and go.

Young Roman It's heavy. I can carry it in.

Mrs Damrosch Leave it. Don't come any closer. Drop it and go. You
know the rules.

Young Roman You're one of us, and yet you talk like one of them.

Mrs Damrosch I do my job—just like you do yours. And I'm not one of you. My grandmother was German.

Young Roman So why are you here, then?

Silence.

YOUNG ROMAN dumps the sack and leaves.

MRS DAMROSCH locks the gate as MAMA enters.

Mrs Damrosch This is the courtyard.

Mama It's so bare.

Mrs Damrosch I scrub it every Tuesday and Friday.

Mama I don't expect you to—

Mrs Damrosch Commandant's orders. His wife is holding a dinner party for you and your husband tomorrow evening. I'll press your evening dress in the morning.

Mama Evening dress? I didn't think I'd need one.

Mrs Damrosch There are functions every week. You could drive to Biala tomorrow. There are some shops still open.

Mama No. Thank you.

Mrs Damrosch Then we must make do with what we have.

PAPA enters.

Your new home is to your satisfaction, sir?

Papa Yes. Most… satisfactory.

Mrs Damrosch Hardly the style you are accustomed to. But sacrifices must be made.

Papa Yes.

Mrs Damrosch Breakfast is served at seven-thirty.

Mama I think I can do that—

Mrs Damrosch The Commandant wouldn't hear of it. Now, if that's all, I'll bid you goodnight.

Papa Yes. Thank you.

MRS DAMROSCH exits.

Silence.

Mama Why have we come here?

Papa You know why. We could not refuse.

Mama I do not want him to know what is beyond these walls.

PAPA sighs.

What do we tell him? When he asks what is over there?

JAN enters from the house.

Jan I don't like this house. It has no attic. I want to go home.

Gypsy music begins.

Papa Listen. To the music.

Jan Where is it coming from?

Papa From the gypsy camp, on the other side of the wall.

Jan Gypsies? Why are they behind such a high wall? Are they dangerous?

Papa No... No, they're just...

Mama [*covering*] Loud. Very loud. They play their music all night long. So, it's only fair for everyone else that they play behind a wall. People have to sleep.

Papa That's right! Not everyone loves music as much as we do. It is good we are near the gypsies, yes? They are musical people. Like us. Violins, flutes, bells, tambourines... They even have a carousel, for their children.

Jan Can I go there, tomorrow?

Papa No. Not tomorrow...

Jan When?

Mama We'll see.

The lullaby turns into a lament.

Jan Have you ever met a real gypsy, Mama?

Mama No. But I remember, when I was a girl, I would hear them, from deep within the forest near my house. As if the trees were singing. Their sound was strange, exciting. Your Opa would warn me, 'Beware of the gypsies, they dance barefoot, they will lure you to the centre of the forest, steal all of your gold, charm you, and you will never come home'.

Jan So, they are dangerous?

Mama It was just a story. A fairytale.

Jan But Opa didn't like the gypsies?

Mama No one liked the gypsies.

Jan Why not? Did they steal his gold?

Mama Not all stories should be believed, Jan.

Papa Not everyone's memories can be trusted, either.

Mama It is up to you... to make up your own mind. But saying people are bad, without knowing the real story... well, this is unfair. Don't you think?

Jan Yes...

> *A train bellows in the distance.*
> *The lights change.*

Scene Three

The gypsy side of the wall.
VIORICA, ROMAN and ION with instruments.

Ion One more song, Mama?

Viorica No!

Ion One for good luck—?

Viorica Ha! We need more than luck in this place. No! I'm not singing any more. Not tonight. It's cold. My bones are aching. It's not like I'm singing for my supper any more, is it? What does it get me? Huh? Nothing.

Ion Music is our only wealth. It's what I live for. It's my inheritance.

Viorica Your inheritance! Look at where we are!

Ion Without it, I am nothing. [*Caressing his violin*] My good friend.

Viorica Hah! No wonder you never found a woman!

Roman A woman might betray you. A violin... never.

Viorica [*to ION*] Is this what you've been teaching my grandson?

Ion It's true!

Viorica [*to ROMAN*] Don't listen to your uncle. He knows nothing. He lives with his head in the clouds. Even as a baby, he was peculiar. And his ears stuck out.

Ion I was a beautiful child!

Viorica See? There he goes—lying again!

Ion You are so cruel!

Viorica Yes. I know. I'm a nasty old lady. And I'm tired. Tired of pretending that there is a future for us. Tired of singing songs when our friends and family are taken away, never to come back—

Ion They go to another camp. For work.

Viorica Fool! Everyone knows that's not true. Why are you kidding yourself? Why do you think the walls are so high? Huh?

KAPO enters from the darkness. He eats a chunk of bread.

Viorica [*to KAPO*] Who did you kill for that?

Roman Sssh!

Ion He's one of us.

Viorica Hah!

Ion He's just doing what he has to do.

Viorica Enough of your babbling—stupid words—look at where we *are!*

Ion I believe in the goodness of people. I have to. Just as Papa taught me.

Pause.

Viorica Fat lot of good it did him. People don't like other people. That's the truth.

Ion Mama.

Viorica The truth! Look around you. I'm cold. And tired.

VIORICA exits.

Ion Am I wrong? To think these things? In this place?

Roman [*with a shrug*] If it helps… why not?

Ion Where do you think your mama and papa have gone? And my papa?

Roman I don't know.

Pause.

Ion Somewhere better than this place…?

Silence.

ION and ROMAN exit into the darkness.

A train whistles in the distance.

KAPO looks at the stars.

The lights change.

Scene Four

The German side of the wall. Early the next morning.

JAN, carrying a pair of rollerskates, and a box under his arm. PAPA, carrying a satchel.

Papa It's out of the question. Those are the rules.

Jan So what am I supposed to do?

Papa Stay here. With your mama.

Jan So we are prisoners too?

> *PAPA exits through the gate.*
>
> *MAMA enters as JAN moves towards the gate, and reaches to open the latch.*

Mama *No*, you are forbidden to leave this courtyard! [*Dragging him away*] You must never go outside that gate, do you understand? Never.

Jan Yes, Mama.

Mama Promise me.

Jan I promise.

> *JAN coughs violently. It subsides.*
>
> *MAMA embraces him.*

Mama [*gently*] You must be careful, Jan.

Jan If this is such a dangerous place, why did we come here?

Mama [*evasively*] You didn't eat your breakfast.

Jan I didn't like it. Is she cooking for us from now on?

> *MRS DAMROSCH enters, carrying a basket.*

Mrs Damrosch I think I've solved your lack of dinner dress.

Mama Have you?

Mrs Damrosch [*holding up a frilly dress from the basket*] I took it upon myself to remodel one of your dresses. I hope you don't mind. I stayed up all night. I was a seamstress... before... Don't you like it?

Mama Yes... it's... lovely. Thank you.

Mrs Damrosch Good. I'm glad to be of service. It should be quite flattering.

Mama Yes. I'm sure—

Mrs Damrosch I'll collect your provisions from the store now, if that's all right with you?

Mama Yes. Thank you.

> *MRS DAMROSCH exits.*

Poor woman. [*Pause.*] We must think of ways to make the most of our situation, yes? What will we do?

Jan [*holding up his skates*] What about my skates? I won't hurt myself. I promise.

Mama No. Absolutely not. You're not well enough.

Jan But I haven't used them yet!

Mama No! Your opa should have known better. Such a ridiculous present. [*A beat.*] You must do restful things. You're sick.

Jan I feel all right.

Mama No. You're sick. Come inside. We will play cards. Drink tea, and eat the cakes Aunt Berte made... Come.

> *MAMA drags JAN indoors.*

Scene Five

PAPA enters through the gate, followed by ROMAN, VIORICA and ION, carrying their instruments. KAPO also.

Papa This will be much more quiet here, I think. We can get down to business. Please—sit down, if you wish.

> *The GYPSIES do not react. KAPO sits.*

[*Awkwardly*] Right... Well... I'll just go and get the music. I won't be long.

> *He sighs and exits into the house.*

Viorica He's playing a game with us. Or he's an idiot.

Ion I like him.

Viorica He's one of them. They're all the same.

Ion He's left us alone. In his own home. And he asked if we wanted to sit down. No one has ever done that before.

Viorica Mmmmm. Same dog, new tricks.

Roman He's frightened. Like us. I can see it in his eyes.
Viorica Hmm! All the more reason to be wary.

> *JAN enters, skates dangling from his hand.*

Jan [*to ROMAN*] Hello…

> *Silence.*

My name is Jan.

> *Silence.*

What's your name?

> *Silence.*
> *PAPA enters.*

Papa Let us begin. I have some music, just a simple melody for you
to play. If you'd come over here.

> *The GYPSIES stare blankly at the music.*
> *KAPO begins whistling Chopin's 'Funeral March'.*

Right… we'll try it one at a time. Beginning with you… your
name, I'm sorry.
Roman Roman, sir.
Papa Are you ready?

> *Silence.*

Yes?
Jan I don't think he is, Papa.
Papa Jan! [*To ION*] What about you…? Name?
Ion [*shaking his head*] Ion, sir.
Papa [*to VIORICA*] And you? Your name?
Viorica [*shaking her head*] Viorica.
Jan [*in a loud whisper*] Why don't they talk to us?
Papa Jan! [*To the GYPSIES*] The Commandant has selected you,
especially. He tells me your music is a brilliant sound. But if you
refuse to play it… I don't know what we can do. I want to teach
you, but I cannot help… if you do not speak to me.

> *Pause.*

Roman We can't play it. We cannot read music. Sir.

Papa Aaaah…

Roman It is not our way. We learn by listening.

Ion It is an inheritance—

Viorica We're gypsies. We keep it in here.

> *She taps her head.*
>
> *ION plays a flourish on his violin*

Ion Music is a mystery. Not everyone has it. You can study, to be an engineer, a doctor. But for music, you need talent. You have to be born with music in your blood.

Jan I wasn't. I hated piano lessons.

Papa Jan—

Ion There! See? You either like it or not. It cannot be forced on you. You can only do it if you love it. That's why it is so wonderful.

> *ION begins playing a hora (traditional folk dance).*
>
> *ROMAN joins in, and VIORICA sings.*

Viorica [*singing*] I'm in love with Janoska,
  Ay lay la lay lay,
  Much more than a bottle of rum,
  Ay lay la lay lay,
  Janoska also loves me,
  He tears the skirt off me!

> *The song ends abruptly.*
>
> *A stunned silence from PAPA.*
>
> *JAN begins laughing.*

Papa Thank you… Very… enchanting.

Jan Sing another one! 'He tears off my dress!'

> *He laughs uncontrollably.*

Papa Jan! Please—

Jan [*stops laughing*] Yes, Papa.

Papa You are to perform before important men in four weeks time. You must be brilliant.

Roman What music are we to play, sir?

Papa 'Au Fond du Temple Saint', from *The Pearl Fishers*. It's an opera—

Viorica An opera? With my voice? How can I sing an opera?

Ion We are hardly an orchestra, sir.

Viorica This is impossible! You should find someone else.

Roman No! We have no choice. [*To VIORICA*] If we fail, you know what will happen to us. [*To PAPA*] We will learn the music. We will do what they ask of us. We will do our best.

Viorica And how are we to learn this music?

Papa By listening. I have a gramophone recording of the opera. You will listen to the aria—over and over again. Until you know the melody line by heart. [*A beat.*] Yes?

Roman Yes.

Ion Yes.

Viorica [*with a shrug*] Whatever...

Papa Good. We'll start immediately.

> *MAMA enters with cakes and tea.*
> *KAPO whistles. The GYPSIES stare hungrily.*

Jan They should eat first, Papa. They are hungry.

Papa Yes. Of course.

Jan [*gesturing*] Come.

> *The GYPSIES and KAPO move slowly to the table and stare at the cakes.*

What are you waiting for? Eat!

> *The GYPSIES stuff handfuls of cake into their mouths.*
> *The gramophone record begins playing the aria.*
> *JAN watches ROMAN intently. ROMAN smiles, his teeth covered in cake. JAN laughs.*

Old Roman Jan had never seen such a sight before. He did not understand what 'hunger' meant... how people behaved when they are starving for food... But hunger for friendship... how Jan yearned for friendship in that strange place. [*A beat.*] And Roman, also. In a place like that, you become a man very quickly... He had forgotten that he was a boy himself... But in that moment, he remembered. And when he smiled his cakey smile, their lives were altered. Forever.

Scene Six

The courtyard.

JAN sits on the bench, holding the skates. KAPO, asleep in a chair against the wall, is wrapped in a new coat.

The aria is heard from the house.

ROMAN enters, dressed in other clothes.

Jan They're my father's conducting pants.

Roman Your mother gave them to me. Will he mind?

Jan I don't think so. He doesn't conduct any more. But he will again, one day. Perhaps you can give them back to him, when he does.

Roman If I'm still here.

Jan Why? Where are you going?

Roman You don't know, do you?

Jan What? Know what?

> *Pause.*

Roman Sure… I'll give them back to him. One day.

> *KAPO snores.*

Jan Who is he?

Roman [*with a shrug*] A Kapo.

Jan A what?

Roman Kapo. Every barracks has one. They're on both sides. Top of the heap traitors, all of them. They think they're special, just because they wear cast-off boots. He's a prisoner, just like me. He'd sell his own mother for an onion. That's what Kapos do. One day he'll get what's coming to him.

Jan Do you want to try my skates?

Roman I don't know how.

Jan It's easy. Any fool could do it.

Roman If it's so easy, then why don't you do it?

Jan I'm not allowed to. I'm too sick. It's my lungs. I was very sick when we lived in Berlin.

Roman All that city air. No good. You need fresh country air.

Jan Like the air here.

Roman I guess… When the wind is blowing in the right direction.

15

Jan What do you mean?

Roman Aren't you going to show me how it's done?

Jan Oh, no. I couldn't. Mama would be very angry.

Roman She doesn't have to know.

Jan I couldn't. I might hurt myself.

Roman Ha! *Pikonyej!*

Jan What does that mean?

Roman You're a baby!

Jan I am not!

Roman Scared of your own mother!

Jan I am not!

> *ROMAN laughs.*
> *JAN puts the skates on.*

Let me know if you hear Mama coming.

> *JAN stands on shaky legs and pushes himself towards ROMAN.*

See? Who's a baby now?

Roman You're not very good. I bet I could do better.

> *JAN gains confidence and begins gliding around the courtyard.*

Let me have a go.

Jan [*haughty*] No. I don't think I will. I'm having too much fun.

> *ROMAN chases him.*

Roman You're not very fast!

> *JAN stumbles and falls.*
> *ROMAN laughs.*

Jan I've hurt myself.

Roman Here we go again. Cry baby!

Jan I don't think I like you very much.

Roman [*advancing*] Right. You asked for it.

Jan Mama!

Roman [*menacing*] Don't bother calling for her. She won't hear you… It's just you and me…

> *ROMAN begins tickling JAN, who laughs uncontrollably.*

Jan Stop…! Don't…! Stop!

Roman Don't stop? Okay, I won't!

Jan No…! I'll wet myself!

Roman Cry baby.

Jan Please…!

The boys sit next to each other.

Aren't you going to try the skates?

Roman No. I don't want to make a fool out of myself. Like you did.

JAN punches ROMAN. ROMAN punches JAN.

Jan Ow!

Roman Serves you right.

JAN touches ROMAN's arm.

Jan What's that? On your arm?

Roman My number.

Jan What for?

Roman So they know who I am.

Jan B3606… What about your name? Isn't that enough?

Roman No. I'm a prisoner. We all have them.

Jan It's ugly. Can you wash it off?

Roman It's a tattoo. It will never come off.

Jan Did it hurt?

Roman [*with a shrug*] I handled it.

Jan I'd like to go there.

Roman Where?

Jan Over the wall. To the camp.

Roman You're mad.

Jan Will you take me?

Roman No!

Jan Why not?

Roman There's no way.

Jan Please?

Roman No.

Pause.

Jan You can borrow my skates, if you want. Take them with you
back to the camp, and play with them, with your friends.

Roman I have no friends. Everyone's your enemy in this place. You can't trust anybody.

Jan What about your mother and father?

Roman I don't have a mother and father. Not any more.

Jan Why not?

Roman The night we arrived here, they separated us. They led them away. I haven't seen them since.

Jan Do you have any brothers or sisters?

Roman Two sisters. Younger. Dora and Renja. They went with my parents.

Jan Where did they take them?

> *Silence.*

Roman What will we play now?

Jan [*with a shrug*] Cards? A jigsaw puzzle? You want to see my rock collection?

Roman [*chuckling*] Rock collection? You're in another world, aren't you?

Jan What do you mean?

Roman Nothing.

Jan We could read?

Roman No! [*Pause.*] I can't read.

Jan I could teach you.

Roman No. I don't want to.

Jan All right. We won't, then.

Roman I bet you've never felt dirt under your fingernails, have you?

Jan No. Never.

Roman Ever chopped wood, or chased a goat around a field? Or milked a cow?

Jan [*shaking his head*] No. Have you?

Roman Every day. Before they brought us here.

Jan When it's all over, everything will go back to normal.

Roman You really believe that?

Jan Of course. Don't you?

Roman What've your folks told you about this place?

Jan That it's a camp. For prisoners.

Roman That's it?

Jan Yes. Papa didn't want to come here. But they made him. He
doesn't agree with what his country is doing.

Roman He said that?

Jan I overheard him arguing with Mama, before we came here. She
was crying.

Roman You haven't told anyone else?

Jan No.

Roman Don't. It's dangerous. If they found out how your parents
feel, it wouldn't be good. For them. Or you.

Jan Why not?

Roman Think about it! Me, on one side of the wall. You, on the
other. We're enemies.

Jan Not to me, we're not.

Roman But to everyone else? That's what war is. The world is out of
control. People are desperate. Everyone does what they have to
do. Even if they don't like it. It's called survival. If your papa didn't
want to come here, then why didn't he say no?

Jan I don't know.

Roman Ha! I know why.

Jan Tell me.

Roman No. You think about it. Time for you to toughen up.

> *ROMAN playfully punches JAN. JAN punches back.*
> *They repeat, their force growing.*

Roman Ow!

Jan [*laughing*] Ha ha! *Pikonyej!*

> *ROMAN lunges for him and they wrestle playfully.*
> *MRS DAMROSCH enters from the side gate and drops her bags.*

Mrs Damrosch Get away from him!

> *MRS DAMROSCH knocks JAN out of the way to attack ROMAN.*
> *KAPO wakes and watches.*

Jan [*in pain*] My arm!

Mrs Damrosch What do you think you're doing?! You idiot!

Jan Leave him alone! Stop it!

> *MAMA and PAPA enter from the house.*

Papa What is going on?

Jan We were playing! [*Crying*] My wrist…

Mrs Damrosch Is he hurt? [*To ROMAN*] You're done for, boy. If the Commandant finds out— [*To KAPO*] And as for *you*—

Papa That will be enough!

Jan Is it broken, Mama?

Mama Just sprained.

Mrs Damrosch See what you did? Aren't you ashamed?

Jan For what? We were playing!

Mrs Damrosch They were not playing!

Mama If our son says they were, then they were.

Mrs Damrosch If the Commandant hears about this the boy will be punished.

Jan No! He did nothing.

Roman Don't threaten me! You're not so special.

Mrs Damrosch My grandmother—

Roman So what?! You're doomed just like the rest of us!

> *Silence.*

Mama [*to PAPA*] You should return to your work. Take the boys inside.

> *The MEN exit into the house.*

Mrs Damrosch You let them into your house?

Mama Who I let into my house is *my* business. And you, as my servant, have no say in the matter. Is that understood?

Mrs Damrosch But if the Commandant hears of this—

Mama Oh, Mrs Damrosch—

Mrs Damrosch It will not go well… for *me*.

Mama [*understanding*] I see. [*Pause.*] Well, the more reason to keep it a secret, don't you think? He won't hear a word from us, if that's what you're afraid of.

Mrs Damrosch Thank you, madam.

Mama Like you, Mrs Damrosch, we are not here at our own choosing. We must do the best we can, and trust one another, don't you think?

Mrs Damrosch Yes. Of course. Thank you, madam.

MRS DAMROSCH begins to exit but halts as VIORICA enters, dressed in the fur-lined frock.

That dress—

Viorica [*proudly*] It's beautiful, isn't it? I've never seen such a beautiful dress before.

Mrs Damrosch I'll start lunch... For *six* people?

Mama Thank you, Mrs Damrosch.

MRS DAMROSCH exits.

The lights change.

Scene Seven

Old Roman And so they practised their music every waking hour. The days passed by. The boys spent many hours together. Winter began to make way for spring... a hint of clear blue skies. A promise... of something... a change? There were rumours that the Russians were on their way to liberate the camp... But in that place, promises didn't exist... And the only thing that changed, was the direction of the wind.

A train whistles in the distance.

Early evening.

KAPO is against the wall, asleep. JAN teaches ROMAN to read. MRS DAMROSCH paints VIORICA's nails.

Music emanates from inside.

Roman [*reading*] One... evening... there... was a... terr—a terri—

Jan Terrible.

Roman A terrible... storm... Thunder?

Jan [*nodding*] Uh-huh. Good.

Roman Thunder rolled... light-ning... flashed... and the rain came... pouring... down—

Rapid gunfire sounds in the distance.

Jan [*startled*] What is that?

Roman What did it sound like?

Jan A gun.

Roman Then a gun it is.

MAMA enters.

Mama You should come inside.
Jan No. I don't want to.
Mama But it's cold. You're not well.
Jan No! I'm all right! Leave us, we're busy.
Viorica Look at my nails!
Mrs Damrosch Keep blowing on them. You'll smudge them.

MAMA exits.

Jan Where were we…?
Roman I don't want to read any more. Not today.
Jan But you're doing so well.
Roman I said I don't want to! What are you, deaf as well as dumb?

JAN coughs violently.

Your mama is right. You should be in bed, resting.
Jan But I want to be with you.
Roman You're crazy. If I had a warm bed, I'd never get out of it. I'd stay there forever.

The sound of gunfire.
KAPO wakes.

Mrs Damrosch Shall we go inside?

The WOMEN exit indoors.

Jan What's wrong?
Roman Nothing.

ROMAN stands and begins pacing.

Jan Is it the gunfire?
Roman You wouldn't understand.
Jan Why do you always do that? I asked Papa why we came here… what would have happened to us if he'd said no. He told me I didn't need to know. So did Mama. That's why I know nothing. No one tells me anything.

Smoke blows in from over the wall.

Smoke. Ugh! What are they burning?

ROMAN turns as white as a sheet.
KAPO whistles the 'Funeral March'.
Ash begins to fall from the sky.

It's snowing. But it's warm.

Roman All day long the trains arrive. You've heard them. Full of people. Where do you think they go?

Jan I don't know.

Roman They walk them up the avenue. A long line. Thousands of them. It's a one-way street. No one ever comes back.

Jan Perhaps they go to another part of the camp.

Roman I've seen a mountain made of shoes. Under the chimneys. Where do you think their owners have gone?

Jan I don't know.

Roman I do. They go to the ovens. Where they took my mama and papa. And my sisters. And my grandpapa. And everyone else. Turned to cinders. And sooner or later, my turn will come.

Jan No! No! It won't! It can't!

Roman The camp is getting emptier. It's only a matter of time.

Jan You could escape…?

Roman Where would I go? There's only one way out of here. I know what my future is.

Jan Why don't you fight? Why doesn't anyone fight?

Roman With what? We're not an army. We have nothing to fight with. We have become what they think we are. Animals. Everyone for himself.

Jan I'd fight!

Roman Not for long, you wouldn't.

Jan I would! I would.

Roman One night, the skies are going to explode with the light of our saviours. A million fighter planes, Russians, Americans… I don't care who… dropping their bombs… on the ovens… the electric fences, the high walls, the train lines… And then I'll see my family again. They'll be waiting for me… in a field of green grass… Sure. I dream. But that's all it is. A dream. They won't be waiting for me. There'll be no sign of them. Not even a grave, a pile of stones, a marker. Nothing.

JAN gets his rock collection from the table.

What are you doing?

JAN places a rock on the ground before them.
VIORICA and ION enter silently, with their instruments.

Jan This is for your papa.

ROMAN places a rock on top of the other.
JAN continues placing rocks in a line.
VIORICA and ION begin playing a lament.

Roman For Papa...
Jan This is for your mama.
Roman For Mama...
Jan Your grandpapa...
Roman Grandpapa...
Jan And your sisters...
Roman Dora... and Renja...

The boys complete their work and stand hand in hand.
ROMAN cries.

Jan [*gently*] Maybe they're angels now. In heaven. Watching you.

VIORICA sings 'Keserves'.

Viorica [*singing*] *Elment a madarka...*
Jan What is she saying?
Roman The bird has flown away.
Viorica [*singing*] *Üres a kalitka...*
Roman The cage is empty...
Viorica [*singing*] *Azt üznte vissza...*
Roman A message has arrived...
Viorica [*singing*] *Vissza jö tavaszra...*
Roman Someone will return in the springtime...
Viorica [*singing*] *Ha tavaszra nem jö...*
Roman If he doesn't return in the springtime...
Viorica [*singing*] *Szölö lágyulásra...*
Roman He will return when the grapes are turning soft...
Viorica [*singing*] *Ha akkorra sem jö...*

Roman If he does not return when the grapes are turning soft...
Kapo Ssshhh!

> *The song ceases.*
> *The sound of planes.*
> *MRS DAMROSCH, MAMA and PAPA enter.*
> *Everyone looks up.*
> *The planes draw nearer.*

Jan The song... How does it end?
Ion The stars! Look at the stars!
Mrs Damrosch Sweet Jesus!
Viorica They're not stars, you idiot!
Ion To me they are!
Jan How does it end?
Roman It's the fighter planes! Millions of them!
Viorica Look at the lights! They look just like my nails!
Ion They come to liberate us! Look at the sparkles!
Mrs Damrosch [*terrified*] They'll kill us.

> *ION plays a dance, as bombs fall in the distance.*
> *KAPO grabs MRS DAMROSCH and begins dancing, twirling her*
> *around the courtyard.*

Stop it! Stop it! Please! You're making me dizzy!

> *Sirens blare around the camp.*
> *MRS DAMROSCH runs into the house.*

Papa You should return to the camp, all of you—
Jan No! I want to know how the song ends!
Mama Jan—
Papa Go now. Quickly.
Jan No, Papa! Let them stay with us! Roman—how does it end?

> *The GYPSIES exit.*

Why do you send them back?
Papa Jan.
Jan I know where we are! I know what they do here!
Mama Ssshh. Calm yourself.

Jan I hate you! For bringing me here! For letting this happen! For being a part of it! For letting all of those people... I hate you!

> *JAN runs into the house.*
> *The sirens blare.*

Scene Eight

Old Roman The planes flew away. No one was saved. And life went on... But not in the same way. The enemy was advancing. Russians, Americans. It felt as if the earth's axis would shift at any moment. Fear, like a ripple, spread through the camp—on both sides of the wall. Roman and his family played louder than ever before. When you're that hungry... for promise, for life... you relish even the smallest of crumbs. Everyone thought, 'The next time they come back, they'll win'. Freedom. Or maybe not.

> *The GYPSIES begin playing 'Au Fond du Temple Saint'.*
> *PAPA conducts.*

Disease spread. Death no longer discriminated between the winners or the losers. Jan became very sick. His body wracked with illness, and infested with lice. He battled time. Win, or lose? Fight or flight...? And still the chimneys smoked...

> *Night-time.*
> *KAPO sits against the wall, eyes closed.*
> *The GYPSIES continue to play the aria.*
> *MAMA watches.*
> *Gunfire sounds from over the wall.*
> *The aria ends. MAMA applauds.*

Papa Excellent!
Mama Bravo! That was beautiful.

> *Distant shellfire.*

Roman Do you really think there'll be a concert?
Papa We must continue, as if there will be.
Ion There won't be. We'll soon be free. You'll see. We'll go home.
Viorica Watch your mouth! Remember who you're talking to!

Ion [*humbled*] I'm sorry, sir.

> MRS DAMROSCH enters.

Mrs Damrosch The Commandant has gone. Left us.
Papa Gone?
Mrs Damrosch 'The enemy will be here within days', they're saying. They're emptying the barracks. They're marching us to other camps. Or sending us to the our deaths in the ovens. One or the other. [*Crying*] Please help me! Take me with you when you go.
Mama [*to PAPA*] We can't. Jan is too sick to move.
Papa No. We will not run. We will stay here and wait.
Mrs Damrosch If you are caught—
Papa I've done nothing wrong! I was made to come here! As you were. Threatened. No. We will not run. It will do us no good.
Mrs Damrosch But how am I to escape? On foot? I will not go back there! They've taken everything from me, but I will not let them take my life! Please—help me.

> PAPA looks to the GYPSIES.

Papa [*to MRS DAMROSCH*] Can you drive, Mrs Damrosch?
Mrs Damrosch Yes.
Papa Then you can take our car.

> MRS DAMROSCH is awe-struck into silence.

On one condition. You take two of them [*the GYPSIES*] with you.
Viorica Two?
Papa That's all there is room for. I'm sorry. [*To MRS DAMROSCH*] Hide them in the trunk of the car. Until you are away from danger.

> Pause.

Mrs Damrosch We must hurry.
Ion I'll stay.
Viorica No!
Roman No! I'm stronger than you. I can stay and fight. I'll live.
Ion I've waited this long… What's a few more days? You're young. You need to be strong now. For your grandmama.
Viorica You're all I have left… my only child…

Ion One day soon, you'll see me walking up the road. You'll be in the field, chasing the goats. You'll wave to me…

Viorica My baby…

Papa You must come now. To the side door.

Ion One day soon…

> *They exit into the house.*
>
> *ION gazes after them.*
>
> *Gunfire continues to be heard.*
>
> *ION exits slowly.*
>
> *A pause.*
>
> *JAN enters from the house wrapped in a blanket.*

Jan … Where is everybody?

> *Silence.*

Where are they? Where's Roman?

Kapo Gone.

Jan Where? Where!?

> *KAPO whistles the 'Funeral March'.*

I have to save him… I said I'd fight for him!

> *JAN runs from the courtyard through the gate.*
>
> *KAPO stands and exits after him.*
>
> *Close shelling.*
>
> *The lights change.*

Scene Nine

In the camp. Night-time.

Distorted carousel music plays. Random gunfire is heard.

OLD ROMAN's face is illuminated. Behind him, JAN walks alongside the wall.

The air is thick with smoke.

Old Roman And so, Jan entered hell. Or the nearest thing to it on earth. He wandered, blinded by all he saw. The walking dead, the bodies frozen on the ground, the fate of strangers… [*He sighs.*]

28

How can anyone live so close to such misery, and not know of its existence?

Jan [*calling*] Roman!

Old Roman Lost in the maze, he wandered for what seemed like an eternity... Through the thick, rank smoke, he saw the mountain of shoes...

Jan [*yelling*] Roman! Roman!

> *ION enters.*

Ion You must go back. It's not safe here.

Jan Where is he?

Ion He's gone—

Jan How does the song end?

Ion What?

Jan What will happen to me? When the enemy comes? What will they do to me?

Ion You're papa and mama will keep you safe. Go back to them.

Jan They're murderers! They're just like all the others.

Ion No. They are good people. You must go back to them...

Jan I never want to see them again...

> *The carousel grinds to a halt. Silence.*
>
> *The squeak of KAPO's boots surrounds and disorientates them. KAPO whistles the 'Funeral March'.*
>
> *He steps from the shadows and advances to JAN.*

What do you want?

Kapo [*indicating JAN's blanket*] Give me that blanket. I'm cold.

Jan No.

> *KAPO grabs JAN. They struggle.*
>
> *The sound of gunfire.*
>
> *KAPO falls to the floor.*
>
> *PAPA enters from the darkness, a gun in his hand.*
>
> *MAMA follows.*

Papa Come away from him.

Jan You killed him!

Papa I did it to protect you.

Jan Look around you! Look at what you've protected me from! Look at what we've done!

Papa You're my flesh and blood! I love you. I had no choice—

Jan Everyone has a choice. Right or wrong.

Mama Jan. Please.

Jan I hate you!

Papa Don't do this.

Jan You lied to me! You disgust me! I never want to see you again!

JAN runs away into the darkness.

Mama [*howling*] Jan! Jan!

Papa [*calling*] Jan!

PAPA exits after him.

MAMA moves slowly off into the madness, sobs wracking her body.

Gunfire and shelling continues in the distance.

ION moves to KAPO and takes his boots. He stands, then marches back and forth in high goose-steps. He smiles broadly.

Scene Ten

OLD ROMAN and TOBY.

Old Roman Jan never saw his parents again. He walked out of the camp... with everyone else... on the death march. It was his way out, Toby. He walked for weeks, whilst others perished on the sides of the road... Then one night, as everyone slept, the army abandoned them... left them... in the middle of nowhere... Freedom... silent and strange... rose with the sun on that cold morning... There was no laughter... no songs... just hushed questions... about which way was home...

Toby But what about you, Granddad? What happened to you?

Old Roman *That* is what happened to me. My name was Jan. Jan Klein-Rogge. Until I changed it.

Toby You're the German boy?

Old Roman I walked south with a group of survivors, Jews, gypsies, political prisoners... I was free. So I walked... and walked... to the edge of the sea. But it was not far enough. [*He rolls up his sleeve.*]

The night before I boarded the ship to come to this country, I had it tattooed on my arm. B3606. I became him. Took his name. It was the only way I could remember him… You're ashamed of me now.

Toby No. I—You were one of them.

Old Roman I was a child. A child of a country seduced by the beautiful words of a dictator. But the beauty soon turned to fear. And the world began to spin out of control…

The GYPSIES play and sing 'Keserves'.

A spinning top does not stop suddenly. It grinds down. And it still hasn't stopped… not yet. There are wheels within wheels… So many layers… of hate… and loss… and hope… I believe in hope, Toby… still. [*He sighs.*] Or perhaps I'm just a silly old man… trying to remember the words to a song…

The GYPSIES cease singing. OLD ROMAN sits forward.

How does the song end? How does it end?

The lights go out.

END OF PART ONE

From left: Jacqy Phillips as Lurl, Dennis Olsen as Alf, Stephen Sheehan as Saul, Tim Morgan as Ari, Andreas Sobik as Victor and Kim Liotta as Pearl in the 2006 Oddbodies Theatre Company production in Adelaide. Part 2: Pantheon. (Photo: Tony Lewis)

Part 2:

Pantheon

Characters

Actor 1:   **Alf**, late 60s

Actor 2:   **Trent**, 13

Actor 3:   **Sheree Jefferies**, early 40s

Actor 4:   **Victor**, early 40s

Actor 5:   **Pearl**, early 50s

Actor 6:   **Lurline**, early 60s

Actor 7:   **Ari**, 14

Actor 8:   **Saul Greenberg**, 40s

Actor 9:   **Harry**, late 30s

Setting

Australia.
1. The present. A lecture hall.
2. Three and a half years before. Interior of the Pantheon Cinema, Herring Bay, north-western Australia.
3. An open field.
4. Same as 1.
5. Three months after 2. Interior of the Norton Detention Centre.

Scene One

A lectern in a spotlight.
SAUL steps up to it.

Saul Thank you all for coming to hear me speak. I'm Saul Greenberg, I am an author and photographer... and I am an obsessive activist and campaigner for the rights of refugees everywhere.

   Pause.

   If any of you are suspicious of my accent—as a lot of people are nowadays, let's face it—just remember that we're not *all* warmongers, okay? Just because the politicians make a decision, doesn't mean we all agree with it. Right? In fact I never agree with it. Which makes me very unpopular... back home. But enough about that...

   Pause.

   I must say it's great to see so many young people here before me. You—the future of our planet. Let's hope it's not too messed up when you guys take over, huh? Nice to see you've dragged your moms and dads along, too. My mother is here with me, too.

   He points behind him.

   She's back there. Everybody wave to my mom. [*He waves.*] Hiya, Mom! She's my 'roadie'. When you're ready, Mom. I'm going to start with an enchanting story. A story of hope...

   A slide projects onto the wall. It is ARI, smiling.
   The houselights dim.

   This is Ari. He's a wonderful boy, with an amazing zest for life. I had the pleasure of meeting him when I paid a visit to the northern coast of Western Australia. When I took this photo of him, he was fourteen years of age, and he comes from Kabul, in Afghanistan. He and his family escaped the Taliban regime at enormous financial and personal cost. Like so many others, their entire life savings were spent on a bid for freedom. Their careers, friends and families, all left behind. Can you imagine what that must be like…? Maybe some of you have done it, or your parents, or their parents… so maybe some of you know what I'm talking about… Heading towards that dreamland… just like Ari and his family.

Pause.

But his family didn't make it. His uncle, mother, and baby sister all drowned when the boat they were on sank off the northern coast of Australia. There were over three hundred and fifty refugees on that boat. Only Ari, and twenty-two others, survived.

Pause.

Ari is what the Australian Government calls a SUNC—No, it's not a joke. It's an acronym: Suspected Unlawful Non-Citizen. SUNC. And the boats have been given the title of SIEV: Suspected Illegal Entry Vessel. SIEV. SUNC. Quite unfortunate titles, aren't they?

Pause.

If you think Ari walked out of the ocean and into the arms of the coastguard… and thrown into detention immediately—think again. Ari's is an amazing story, lemme tell ya. I should know—I was there…

The lights change.

Scene Two

Inside the Pantheon Cinema. High walls flaking with grandeur. Chairs set in rows facing the audience. A table set up with refreshments.

The final moments of The Wizard of Oz, *watched by VICTOR, ALF, TRENT, LURLINE and PEARL, dressed as Glinda and Dorothy respectively. The film ends.*

All [*sighing*] Aaaaaaw…
Pearl Wasn't that bewdiful?
Lurline Are you crying? Again? You've seen it every week since you were five!

Pearl I still can't believe it was just a dream. It spoils it somehow. That she goes back to black and white. Like real life is boring. Life isn't black and white.

Alf Huh. Ever been to Manchester?

Pearl My life isn't black and white.

Trent I like the colour bit in the middle.

Lurline Yairs. And we love Judy Garland.

Pearl Love Judy. Adore Judy.

Lurline Yairs. A real talent.

Alf Pure class. They don't make them like they used to. Movie stars.

Pearl [*dramatically*] She's a shining star, still flickering brightly upon the horizon of fame, above the sea of immortality…

> *She giggles.*

Alf Ooh la la! Very posh!

Lurline Did you just make that up?

Pearl Yes.

Lurline Thought so.

Pearl Did you like it, Victor?

Victor Yes. Very much. I never tire of seeing it.

Pearl It's a shame we don't have any Bosnian films. We don't show many, do we, Lurl?

Lurline We don't show any, Pearl.

Pearl No. We don't… do we?

Trent How would we understand them, anyway?

Victor Subtitles. You read the words as you watch.

Trent How can ya see what's happenin'?

Victor You train your eyes. You get used to it.

Trent Jeez. Listen to that wind…

Pearl 'Hope our cinema doesn't blow away!'

Trent 'Auntie Em, it's a twister!'

> *They laugh.*
> *PEARL turns off the projector.*

Lurline Take more than a twister to lift this place over the rainbow. Solid as a rock. Not so good for you fellas, out in your caravans. [*A beat.*] Remember the cyclone back in sixty-nine, Pearl?

Pearl Oooh, yes! Irene Shadbolt lost her annex.

Lurline And Trixie, her fox terrier.

Pearl Oooh, yes... poor Trixie!

Lurline Mmm... Whiney little thing she was... Like a mosquito on a leash.

Trent [*to ALF*] Hope your caravan don't blow away.

Alf My caravan won't be goin' anywhere. Not since I poured a slab around it. Fixed firm. Glued to terra firma. I'll be all right.

Trent You can always move in with me and Mum and Dad. If it blows away.

Alf Taa very much, lad. But I think I'll be all right.

Trent What's on tomorrow night, Pearl?

Pearl Something very special.

Trent What?

Pearl *Casablanca*!

Trent Is it black and white?

Lurline Yairs.

Pearl It's a classic. Bogart and Bergman!

Victor A romance.

Pearl Yes. Lovely.

Alf [*singing*] You must remember this,
    A kiss is still a kiss,
    A thigh is just a thigh...

Lurline [*chuckling*] Yairs.

Trent We should watch *Star Wars* or *ET*, *Raiders of the Lost Ark*.

Lurline Oooh, yairs. Indiana Jones. What a dish.

PEARL giggles.

Trent I like the bit where the bad guy's face melts.

Pearl Oooh.

Lurline This crown's killing me, Pearl.

Pearl Careful. I made it out of old pot scourers. It could snag your hair.

Lurline Ouch! Leave it!

Alf [*yawning*] Well, back to me two-wheeled palace. I must up at crack of sparrow's fart for the early catch. Until tomorrow, sweet starlets!

He kisses PEARL's hand.

Enchante!

Pearl   Yeah. Me too.

   ALF exits.

   [*With a sigh*] Ah, well… another night of enchantment passes
   by… I always get sad when they end.

Victor   Just think of the other nights ahead of us.

Pearl   [*giggling*] I can hardly wait!

Lurline   'Bout time we had a Bette Davis movie. Or a Joan Crawford.
   Mean and nasty women. Somethin' with a bit of grit and guts.

Pearl   Ooooh! Bette and Joan! Love Bette and Joan!

Lurline   Yairs. Rotten to the core. Every time.

Pearl   Marvellous!

Lurline   Adore 'em!

Trent   Can I get a Milo?

Pearl   Yairs. 'Course. What time do you have to be home, darlin'?

Trent   Dunno. Mum and Dad are at the pub.

Lurline   You can stay the night if you like. Plenty of room to kip
   down here.

Trent   [*smiling*] I like stayin' here.

Pearl   Yeah. We have fun. Don't we? You're like the son we never
   had, isn't he, Lurl?

Lurline   Yairs.

Pearl   I would have liked a child to call my own. I used to imagine
   that one would just fall from the sky. Carried by the wind. And it
   would drop. Into my arms. [*With a sigh*] Never mind. S'est la vee!
   Que sera sera…

Trent   Never too late. A tall dark stranger could ride into town on a
   horse. He could take ya on a hot date! You could go neckin' in the
   back row.

Lurline   [*laughing*] Good Lord! No thank you. Rather a cup of tea and
   a good book, thanks very much.

Trent   Borin'. I hate readin'.

Victor   It is the best way to learn. If you know how to read, you can
   learn anything. When we lived in Pristina, I had a room full of
   books. Four walls. Covered in books. They are my passion. Along
   with movies. But my books… doorways into other worlds. [*Pause.*]
   I had to leave them. Like everything else. Run away from it all.
   But when I close my eyes… I can still see them… can still see the

names on every spine… like a photograph… But now I have the movies! They are my doorways, now. My escape.

Trent You just left them? You didn't take any?

Victor Only one. English dictionary. I thought it may be useful. I still have it.

The wind roars outside and the door blows open.

HARRY stands in the doorway.

Pearl [*gleeful*] Harry!

Lurline Hello, love.

Harry How ya doin'?

Lurline All the better to see you, darlin'.

She kisses him.

Harry What are you wearing?

Lurline I'm Glinda. Can't you tell?

Harry I've got someone with me. Is that okay?

Lurline 'Course!

HARRY exits.

Pearl An unexpected guest! I wonder who it is?

Lurline Wait, and you'll find out.

HARRY enters, followed by SAUL.

Saul [*as he enters*] Holy cow! It's like Armageddon out there! Hiya!

Lurline & Pearl [*together*] Hello.

Harry Everyone—this is Saul Greenberg. This is Lurline and Pearl.

Saul The famous sisters.

Pearl Famous? Are we?

Saul Absolutely. He talked non-stop about you all the way from Darwin. [*Looking around*] Far out! He talked about this too. This is a-mazing! How gor-geous! How lucky are you guys—living in *this*.

Lurline Yairs. We wouldn't change it for quids.

Pearl We love it.

Saul Sure. Who wouldn't? Where do you keep all your movies?

Lurline In here. Come on, I'll show you.

LURLINE, PEARL and SAUL exit.

Trent Gidday, Harry.

Harry Trent! How are you, mate?

Trent Yeah, good.

Harry How are you, Victor?

Victor I am doing well, thank you. Very pleased to see you.

Harry [*with a sigh*] It's good to be back. I've been hanging out for a decent movie.

Trent You want a Milo?

Harry Yes, thank you.

LURLINE, PEARL and SAUL enter.

Saul You've got every film ever made in there...

Lurline [*cackling*] Not quite.

Harry Saul, this is Victor... and this is Trent.

They greet each other.

Pearl So, what do you do, Saul?

Saul I'm a writer and political activist.

Lurline & Pearl [*together*] Ooooh!

Saul I write about children mostly. True stories. How war affects them. How their lives are torn apart. Child refugees.

Victor I work, sometimes, as a doctor, in the Detention Centre.

Saul Yes. Harry told me.

Victor These are no places for children... or adults. Not welcoming. Or comforting. Not what is needed. Changes must be made.

Saul That's what I'm fighting for.

Trent You want a Milo?

Saul Do I want a Milo? Sure. What's a 'Milo'?

TRENT passes cups of Milo.

Trent So, Saul—where do you live?

Saul New York.

Trent Caw. What's it like?

Saul Big. Loud. Annoying. Infuriating. Dirty. And I love it. It reminds me every day of what a mad world I live in.

Trent Yuk! Sounds awful.

SAUL laughs.

Lurline [*to HARRY*] How come you're back so soon?

Harry Another boatload of refugees. Left Indonesia about a week ago. The paper wanted me to cover it. So here I am. At the centre of the universe. Again.

Victor How many people this time? On the boat?

Saul Two hundred, three hundred, maybe. Middle-eastern.

Lurline Tsk.

Pearl Families. Floating around. Out there. Somewhere.

Victor On a night like this…

Lurline Poor people…

ALF enters, breathless.

What is it, love?

Alf There's a boy. On the beach. I think he's dead.

The lights change.

Scene Three

ARI is asleep on the couch.
The others stand over him. VICTOR attends to him.

Pearl [*whispering*] It's a miracle.

Lurline He awright?

Victor Yes. Just exhausted.

Trent Do you think there'll be others? Other survivors?

Harry Who knows?

Saul I don't like their chances. In this weather.

Alf Poor kid.

Trent He must be hungry.

Pearl Can we keep him, Lurl? For our very own?

Lurline No, love. 'Course we can't. You know that.

Pearl But he's just a boy. And he came to *us*, Lurl. Blown in. Like a blossom on the wind. Like a cornflake in a blender!

Lurline Calm down! We'll look after him. Just for tonight. And then, in the morning, we'll have to hand him over.

Pearl They'll lock him up!

Lurline Stop getting yourself all worked up.

Victor You know you can't keep him.

Pearl We could hide him.

Lurline Where?

Pearl The Wurlitzer shaft?

Lurline Oh, yes! I can imagine the headlines—'Weirdo Sisters Hide Asylum Seeker in Wurlitzer Shaft'.

Pearl We're not weird… Are we?

Lurline Well…

Harry You can't, Pearl. It's not fair. On you, or the boy.

Saul Or his parents, if they're still alive.

Alf Besides, you'd never be safe from Sheree Jefferies.

> *Groans from all around.*

Saul Who's Sheree Jefferies?

Lurline Owns the general store and post office out on the western side of town. Dreadful woman. Considers herself the coastguard for the area. No one escapes her radar.

Victor She's forever on the phone to the police. She even reported me, when I first came here. I was 'acting suspiciously'. I was only collecting my mail. It was my accent, I expect.

Trent She'd dob ya in if she knew.

Pearl Our very own wicked witch of the west.

Saul [*grimly*] Wow. May I never meet her.

Harry We should go look along the beach. In case there are any others.

> *The MEN exit.*

Pearl [*crying*] Poor thing.

Lurline There there. Ssshhh…

Trent I wonder what his name is?

> *They stare at ARI, bewitched.*
>
> *The lights change.*

Scene Four

TRENT is asleep on floor. ARI is asleep on couch.

Thunder. A Muslim prayer is heard.

TRENT wakes.

Trent Wha? You awright?

ARI shivers.

You cold? You need to keep warm.

Ari Nasreem?

Trent Huh?

Ari Nasreem?

Trent I don't understand. Are you hungry? [*He mimes eating.*] Hung-ry.

> *ARI stares blankly at TRENT, who moves to the table and mixes him a cold Milo.*
>
> *ARI moves to him and watches.*

Milk.

> *ARI touches the milk.*

Milo.

> *ARI touches the Milo tin.*
>
> *Thunder.*
>
> *ARI hides under the table.*

It's only thunder.

> *Silence.*

Here. Drink this.

> *ARI takes the Milo and drains the glass, then offers it back for a refill.*

Ari Hungly mik miro.

Trent [*smiling*] Yeah. Good.

> *The lights change.*

Scene Five

ARI is asleep under table.
LURLINE, PEARL, TRENT and ALF.

Trent Three glasses of Milo and he crashed.

Alf He was probably in the water for hours.

Pearl He needs to rest for a bit longer. Here.

Lurline No. He needs to be looked after. Properly.

Sheree [*offstage*] Hell-oo!

Lurline Oh God! It's Sheree!

> *LURLINE stands in front of the table and throws her skirt over it, hiding ARI.*
>
> *TRENT, ALF and PEARL stand either side of her.*
>
> *SHEREE enters. She surveys the scene.*

Hello, Sheree. How are you?

Sheree Oh, I shouldn't complain. Everything all right here?

Lurline Yairs!

Trent, Pearl, Alf Yairs. Mmm. Good.

Lurline You're early.

Sheree Yes. I've got a social club meeting at ten. So I'm doing the deliveries early. How are you, Alfred?

Alf I'm fine, thanks, Sheree.

Sheree Good.

> *HARRY and SAUL enter, and the group signal wildly that they're hiding ARI.*

And who are you?

Harry I'm Harry.

> *He offers his hand, but it is refused.*

Saul Hiya! I'm Saul.

Sheree You're not from round these parts?

Saul No—I'm from—

Sheree Alfred, the deliveries are in the back of the van, if you'd be so kind.

> *ALF sighs and exits.*

You sure everything's all right here?

Lurline Yairs!

All Yes!

Sheree That's a very… full skirt, you're wearing, Lurl. Did you make it, Pearl?

Pearl Uh-huh. You like it?

Sheree A bit lopsided in the waist, isn't it?

45

Pearl Is it?

Sheree Yes. It's all twisted. It should hang straight. [*She advances.*] Here, let me fix it—

Lurline *No!*

SHEREE stops.

I mean... don't. You can't. Touch it.

Sheree Why not?

Lurline Because—

Pearl It's—

Harry Not finished. It's just pinned together.

Lurline Yairs. That's it.

Pearl You don't want to tear it, do you?

Sheree I wouldn't, Pearl. I have delicate fingers. Unlike you. [*Searching in her handbag*] Here's your mail...

She throws the mail to PEARL.

Pearl Oooh, look. They're all stuck down with sticky tape. Again.

Sheree Yes. They got wet. Sorry.

VICTOR enters.

Everyone signals to him of ARI's hiding spot.

[*Grunting*] Gidday.

Victor Good morning.

Sheree Apparently there was trouble at the Centre last night? Is that true?

Victor I wouldn't know. I wasn't there.

Sheree So ungrateful. We give them a roof, a bed, food—

Saul And you think that's enough?

Sheree It's better than nothing. They should be more thankful.

Victor It's nothing more than a prison.

Sheree Well, it pays you a wage, so I wouldn't whinge about it too much. They broke the rules. They deserve to be locked up. Simple.

ALF enters with boxes of food.

Thanks, Alfred. Very cavalier of you.

Alf Mmmm.

Sheree [*to TRENT*] Is that your dragster outside?

Trent Yeah. Why?

46

Sheree Have you been doin' burnouts outside my shop?

Trent Nah. Why?

Sheree 'Cause the skidmarks are about as wide as your back tyre.

Saul [*laughing*] You measured them?

Sheree It's nothing to laugh about. I have barely enough customers as it is. I don't need hoons scaring them off.

Lurline He's not the only boy in town with a bike, Sheree.

Sheree How come you're over here so early, anyway?

Trent I stayed the night. Mum and Dad were at the pub.

Sheree 'Course they were. Where else would they be? [*Suddenly bright*] So how have you been, Alfred?

Alf Yeah… all right. And it's Alf.

Sheree Alfred is a lovely name. Very… debonair.

Alf Ya think so?

Sheree Absolutely. I can't abide these people who shorten their names, when their full names are perfectly fine. Thankfully I've got a short name. Can't shorten it. 'Hello, my name's Sheree, but you can call me Sh!'

She laughs, but no one joins in.

You want to come to the dance in Norton next Friday night?

Alf Nah. Ta very much.

Sheree Why not?

Alf [*with a sigh*] Don't like dancin'.

Sheree Well, you don't just *dance*. There'll be plenty of people there.

Alf I don't much like them either.

Sheree [*with a sigh*] Right… I'll be on my way, then. Got a lot more ground to cover. So busy. I like to be home with my door locked by sundown.

Saul Why?

Sheree Listen, mate, in case you hadn't noticed, we've got the Detention Centre on one side of us, and the ocean on the other. They could break out or wash up on the beach. Either way you've got trouble.

Saul They scare you?

Sheree I know the drill. [*Waving her mobile phone*] I'm armed. Nothing escapes my attention. They better stay away from my side of town, if they know what's good for them.

Trent They're just people.

Sheree Yeah. Weird people. Weird religion. Weird beliefs.

Saul They're just different. [*A beat.*] A Tibetan lama once explained to me how the spiritual beliefs of the world are like fingers... [*holding up a hand*] ... all separate and independent... but all leading to the palm... to the heart of the matter. All connected. Made me feel... comforted... somehow.

Pearl Oooh, how lovely.

Sheree Yes, well, you won't find many people around here who'd give two hoots for raving lamas. [*To ALF*] I'll see you soon, then, Alfred?

Alf Yeah. I s'pose I will...

Sheree Pearl, Lurl. [*To TRENT*] You and your dragster stay away from my shop, Butterworth—or I'll have you booked.

>   *SHEREE exits.*

Harry I need a coffee after that.

Trent Dad reckons she drives a broomstick.

Victor People like this are impossible.

Lurline Yes. People forget where they come from very quickly. Her parents came here back in the sixties. Pavlukovic, their surname was. Poor as church mice. But they worked. Hard. Proud people, but nice. Sheree changed her name as soon as she was old enough.

Saul From what?

All Ottla.

Lurline She has a problem with where she came from.

Alf She has a problem with everything.

>   *Thunder.*
>   *ARI wakes with a cry.*
>   *TRENT moves to him.*

Trent You're okay... Are you hungry? You want some brekkie?

>   *ARI stares vacantly at him.*

[*Tapping his own chest*] My name is Trent... You?

Ari [*tapping his own chest*] Ari.

Trent Ari. Where are your family? Mama, Papa?

Ari Nasreem.

The sound of heavy rainfall.

Saul What is *that*?

Lurline The rains are here. Two weeks too late. But here now.

Trent I'll bring me dragster in.

Lurline You fellas can kiss goodbye to the thought of goin' anywhere for a while.

Saul Why?

Pearl We'll be flooded in.

Saul Flooded in? You're joking?

Harry Nah, mate. She isn't. There's a river between here and the Detention Centre.

Alf First rainfall it always floods within the hour.

Lurline Without fail. Long as I can remember.

Saul How long does it last for?

Lurline Not long. Only about a week.

Saul [*laughing*] A week?

TRENT brings his dragster indoors.

ARI is entranced by it, and moves to TRENT.

Trent Dragster.

Ari Delagster.

Trent No, dr. Dra.

Ari Dra.

Trent Drag-ster.

Ari Drag-ster.

Trent Yeah. Good. I'll take you for a ride on it, when the weather's better.

Saul So what do you do? When you're flooded in?

Pearl We watch movies, of course. You're very lucky, you made it just in time.

Lurline When we were kids, the first rain of every season, we'd have a movie marathon. Just us, our family. Dad would lock the doors, and Mum would get the projector fired up. Ya remember, Pearl?

Pearl Oooh, yes... And she always made those sausage rolls. The ones with the lovely flaky pastry...?

Lurline Yairs. With homemade tomato sauce. Delicious! Just Mum and Dad and you and me, sittin' in the dark, watchin' the magic, up there, on the silver screen.

Pearl There may be clouds, but they have silver linings in the Pantheon Cinema!

> *LURLINE cackles.*
>
> *PEARL climbs up to the projector box.*

Stations, everyone!

Saul Already?

Harry Just relax and go with the flow...

> *They move to the seats, TRENT guides ARI.*
>
> *The opening music of* Casablanca.

Saul *Casablanca?* I love this movie!

All Ssssh!

Saul [*whispering*] Sorry.

> *ARI stares at the screen. He rises and walks closer to it.*

Film Voice-over Refugees—streaming from all corners of Europe towards the freedom of the new world—across the Mediterranean to Oran—then by train—or auto—or foot—to Casablanca—

Lurline Pass us the Chocolate Royals, Pearl.

Film Voice-over Here the fortunate ones obtain visas and scurry to Lisbon. From Lisbon to the Americas. But the others wait in Casablanca—and wait—and wait—and wait—

Ari Anwait. Anwait. Anwait.

> *The lights change.*

Scene Six

ARI stands staring at the screen.
SAUL talks to the audience.

Saul [*to the audience*] And so Ari rode on the magic carpet to Hollywood—from romance in Casablanca—

Humphrey Bogart Voice-over Here's looking at you, kid...

Saul [*to the audience*] —to the dark jungles of Africa—

> *The sound of Tarzan's signature call.*

—to the Wild West—

> *The sound of cowboys chasing indians.*

—Music. Dancing. Chorus girls—Movie after movie after movie.

Al Jolson Voice-over You ain't heard nothin' yet!

Gene Kelly Voice-over [*singing*] Gotta dance! Gotta dance!

Garbo Voice-over I vant to be alone.

Jimmy Cagney Voice-over Look, Ma! Top of the world!

> *The following lines swirl and overlap.*

Bette Davis Voice-over Fasten your seat belts! It's going to be a bumpy night!

Wicked Witch Voice-over I'll get you, my little pretty, and you're little dog too!

Baron Frankenstein Voice-over It's alive! It's alive!

Bette Davis Voice-over Don't wish for the moon. We already have the stars.

Alec Guiness Voice-over May the force be with you.

ET Voice-over ET, phone home.

> *A stormy babble of famous voices. The room swirls.*

Saul [*to the audience*] For six days and six nights, we watched. Fuelled by cornflakes, toast and Vegemite, Milo and Chocolate Royals... Whilst outside, the rain continued to fall, until the waters flooded the town... But still, we watched... Thursday turned into Friday... And on the seventh day, the rain stopped. The waters subsided...

> *The lights change.*

Scene Seven

Sundown.
ARI stares vacantly at the screen. The projector has stopped.
TRENT, PEARL and LURLINE.

Pearl What's wrong with him, Lurl?

Lurline I don't know. Ari… love?

Trent It's like he can't see us.

Lurline He must be exhausted. I know I am.

Trent All those movies. Don't know how he did it. They all roll into one after the third day.

Lurline My back. We need new seats, Pearl.

SAUL comes in talking on his mobile phone.

Saul [*on the mobile*] Hiya. It's Saul… Yah… I'm fine… Flooded in.

Lurline Your parents know where you are?

Trent Yeah. Rang 'em [*thinks*] Wednesday. Told 'em I was awright.

Lurline They weren't… worried… or anything?

Trent Nah. They never worry about me.

Saul [*on the mobile*] No, we've heard nothing… What did you say happened?

ALF, VICTOR and HARRY enter.

Lurline Well?

Harry Like wading pools.

Lurline Your lovely caravans. What a shame.

Alf Not really. I always wanted to live by the sea when I was a lad. And now I am. I like the surprises it brings. Unexpected.

Harry [*looking towards ARI*] He still hasn't moved?

Pearl Uh-uh.

Saul [*hanging up the mobile*] There's been a riot in the Detention Centre. More than half the detainees have escaped.

Harry Half?

Saul Will we be able to get through in the car?

Harry Sure.

HARRY exits.

Saul Looks like the holiday's over. Off to work for us.

Victor Half the detainees?

Saul That's what he said.

Victor They are desperate. They want their freedom.

Saul You think they'll find it?

Victor No. They'll all be locked up again, with fewer privileges. The world sees these people on their television sets, behind bars, like criminals. But they don't see them up close. Don't see the sadness in their eyes. I must go. They will need me.

Saul Come with us.

HARRY enters.

Harry [*as he comes in*] Ready.

Saul Well—it was lovely to meet you all.

Lurline We'll see you again, won't we?

Harry We'll stay in a hotel at Norton. To be closer. We have to work, now.

Pearl Aw. You'll keep in contact?

Harry Of course. Make sure you call the police. About Ari. Before they call on you.

HARRY, VICTOR and SAUL exit.

Lurline What's wrong with you?

Pearl [*crying*] I hate it when people leave. I want them to stay forever.

Lurline Yairs… I know you do. But nothing lasts forever, pet.

Alf Winter in Manchester makes a good stab at it.

Lurline We should get him in the car.

Trent How? He won't budge.

Lurline Ari? Come on, love.

She tries to pull him, but he hits her away.

Ari [*Cagney*] You dirdy rad!

Silence.

Lurline What did he say?

Ari [*Bogart*] Ear's lookin' ad you, kid…

He crawls behind the chairs.

[*Alec Guinness*] May the fours be wid you.

Trent What's wrong with him?

Ari [*Gene Kelly*] Godda dance! Godda dance!

ARI screams Tarzan's call and runs across the room, as SHEREE enters, dressed for the dance.

She screams.

ARI cowers, sobbing.

[*Edward G Robinson*] Merzy! Is dis de ent of Leeko?

Sheree Who *is* he? Who is he?!

Silence.

Well?!

Silence.

Lurline His name is Ari. He turned up last week. He's all alone—
Sheree What?! You're harbouring an illegal alien?
Trent He's not from Mars!
Pearl He's all alone.
Ari Dirdy rad.
Sheree Shut up!

ARI crawls to TRENT, who comforts him.

Alf Go easy, Sheree. The boy needed rest. We'll hand him over today.
Sheree He's been here all week, you say?
Ari [*Frankenstein*] Iss alive! Iss alive!
Sheree Shut up!
Ari [*Brando*] Stella!
Trent Sssshhh. It's all right.
Sheree That's a criminal offence.

SHEREE takes her mobile phone from her bag.

Alf You going to dob us in, then, or what?
Ari No pace lie home… no pace lie home…
Sheree That all depends on you. Doesn't it?
Lurline That's blackmail.
Sheree No. [*Turning to ALF*] It's called 'how to get what you want'. I called in to see if you'd reconsidered my invitation to the dance, Alfred. Lucky for me I did, eh? [*To LURLINE and PEARL*] I'll give you a couple of hours to get rid of him. By the time Alfred and I return. Is it a deal?

Ari Dirdy rad!

Sheree Well?

    Pause.

Alf All right.

Sheree Good. I'll be waiting in the car. Evening, everyone. Oo-roo!

    SHEREE exits.

Ari Oo-roo!

Pearl [*sobbing*] I hate Sheree Jefferies!

Ari Stella!

Lurline You don't have to do this, Alf.

Alf Don't you worry about me. I'll be all right. You just make sure he's gone by the time we get back.

    ALF exits.

Pearl How can we take him anywhere when he's like this?

Lurline Just sit tight. And stop worrying, you'll make yourself sick. I'm going to call the police.

Pearl But you heard Sheree. We'll be criminals.

Ari No place like home…

Pearl I don't want to go to jail!

Lurline We have to hand him over. He can't stay here any more.

Pearl We can't just push him out there into the dark!

Lurline [*exploding*] Oh, for God's sake, Pearl—*shut up!* I'm so tired of your voice! Sometimes I just want to leave the sound of it and… go away! So many questions. Drives me insane.

    Silence.

Pearl You don't mean that, do you Lurl? You wouldn't really leave me, would you…?

Lurline No… 'Course I wouldn't.

Pearl I'd be lost… all alone…

Lurline Sssh… I won't leave you. I promise. I was just angry. You and me are going to cook a nice meal. Awright? Then we'll… decide what we're going to do. C'mon, you can peel the taters.

    The SISTERS exit.

Ari No pace lie gome… no pace lie gome.
Trent Don't worry. I'll look after ya.

> *TRENT moves to the table and grabs the biscuit tin. He gives it to ARI.*

Trent It'll be better. For everyone.
Ari [*Scarlet O'Hara*] Where I go? Whad I do?

> *TRENT writes a note and leaves it on the table.*
>
> *ARI watches him blankly as he moves to the dragster.*

Delagster.
Trent Uh-huh. We'll be awright, I reckon. You and me.
Ari [*ET*] Ee dee, phone ome…

> *ARI eats a biscuit.*
>
> *The lights change.*

Scene Eight

Later.

ALF enters, followed by SHEREE.

Sheree Well, you've been a miserable dance partner tonight, I must say.
Alf I don't like dancing. I told you that.
Sheree Face like a thunder cloud. Some boyfriend you are.
Alf Cut it out, Sheree! I'm not your boyfriend.
Sheree Oh, I think you are. Your little refugee buddy has seen to that. Still can't work out what possessed you all. Letting him in your home.
Alf I don't know what you've got against them. [*Pause.*] Especially when your own parents were refugees…
Sheree [*frosty*] Lurl and Pearl been telling you all about me, have they?
Alf What does it matter? [*Pause.*] Life has to get pretty bad to leave your home. Your country. Friends. It's an enormous leap of faith. Faith in the future. Faith in the notion that people will be welcoming and accepting. Your parents—just like Ari's, and

just like Victor—did that. Trusted in that. At least your parents survived it… Ari's didn't. Your parents made a go of it. For you. That's something to be proud of, I reckon.

Sheree Oh yes! Proud! I had to be eternally grateful and cheery, about everything. I was never allowed to forget it. Their sacrifice. 'You have no idea what it's like to be hungry! In the war—' 'No, you can't have a new dress—we never had new dresses in the war.' And the names the other kids would call me: Wog. Wop. Commo. I hated having salami sandwiches when everyone else had Vegemite. I hated them. Those people. For not… including me. I just wanted it—*me*—to go away… So I changed my name.

Alf And you've become one of 'Them'. One of 'Those People'.

Sheree [*bitter*] I like who I am!

Alf No, you don't. I'm not going to be your boyfriend. And if you dob my friends in… then that's a choice you'll have to live with. I think you should go home and stand in front of a mirror. Take a good look at yourself.

Sheree You're a fine one to lecture me—with your common-as-muck accent. Where did you come from?

Alf Somewhere else. Just like you. Go home, Sheree. Leave us alone.

LURLINE and PEARL enter. LURLINE holds the note.

What's wrong?

Lurline Trent and Ari… they've gone.

Alf Gone? Where? [*Reading*] 'It is better this way. No trouble for you. I've taken him to freedom on my dragster. Away from danger and Sheree. Trent. P.S. I took some Chocolate Royals.'

Pearl [*sobbing*] This isn't the way it's supposed to be! It's supposed to be a happy ending!

Sheree Get a grip, Pearl! This is real life. Not some silly movie.

Alf We have to find them!

Sheree I'll ring the police.

Alf They're kids, for God's sake! Don't you realise what you've done? I'm going to drive around and have a look.

Pearl Lurl?

Lurline You go with him. I'll check out around here.

ALF and PEARL exit.

I hope you're happy, now.

LURLINE exits.

SHEREE dials her mobile.

Sheree [*on the mobile*] Sergeant Harris?... It's Sheree Jefferies here... Yeah. Another one on the loose... You got a pen?... Be on the lookout for a young boy of middle-eastern descent... It shouldn't be too hard—Trent Butterworth's givin' him a dink on his dragster...

The lights change.

Scene Nine

A distant storm. Pre-dawn. A flat plain.
TRENT and ARI, pushing the bike. Both tyres are flat.
TRENT throws the bike down.

Trent Ugh... I can't go no further... Have to rest... just for a bit.

TRENT lies down. ARI stares about him.
A Salat (a Muslim prayer) is heard.

Ari Allah? Help me?

ARI falls to his knees.

Father? Mother? Nasreem? Where I go? Whad I do?

The sound of a police car siren.
TRENT wakes.

Trent It's the cops! Run for it! Quick! This way!

TRENT and ARI attempt to run, but are blinded by headlights.

Police Voice-over Freeze! Put your hands above your head!

TRENT does so.

Tell the boy to do the same—

Trent Ari. Like me. Same same.

ARI copies TRENT.

58

Police Voice-over Slowly make your way towards the vehicle.

Trent Follow me. You'll be all right...

ARI and TRENT slowly move towards the lights.

Ari I ready for close-up, Mr DeMille...

The lights change.

Scene Ten

SAUL at the lectern.

Saul Ari has been in detention now for two and a half years. Since his capture he has witnessed several major riots—you may have seen them on television or read about them in the papers. Not pretty. A terrifying ordeal for a young boy, all alone, without family, without education, without proper medical care... surrounded by angry men and women, driven to violence by their frustration—they are *so* unhappy, these people. *So* unhappy... No one listens to them... No one hears what they have to say... How would *you* handle that... or *you*... or *you*...?

A slide of ARI, his lips sewn together.

This is how far Ari went—like so many others, he joined the hunger strike... This photo was taken three months after his capture. I received it in the mail, at my apartment in New York. Attached was a note, and in finishing this story, I quote: 'Dear Saul, Smuggled my camera in. The world must see the face of our shame. Use it. Let it be seen. Let it be known that the child has a voice. Let the voice be heard. Yours sincerely... Victor.'

The slide and spotlight fade.
SAUL turns and faces a pool of light, in which ARI lies upon a mattress.
VICTOR crouches over him, cutting the stitches from his mouth.
ARI moans in pain, grabbing VICTOR's arm.

Victor Just one more... that is all... one more...

VICTOR cuts the last stitch.

There... It is finished... It is all over.

Ari Sar—

Victor No no. Ssssh. You must not speak, Ari. Shhh... Rest, hmm?

Ari [*hoarse*] Sar... Sar-wh—

Victor What is it, Ari? What is it you want to say, hmm?

Ari Th-ray—Sar-wh—

Victor Slowly... gently... Tell me...

Ari [*slowly singing*] Sar whair ofer th ray bow—

> Way a pie—
> Birs fie ofer th ray bow—
> Whythen o why carn die...

The lights change.

END OF PART TWO

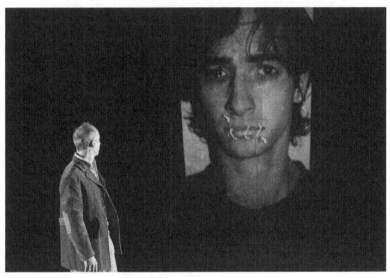

Stephen Sheehan (foreground) as Saul and Tim Morgan as Ari in the 2006 Oddbodies Theatre Company production in Adelaide. Part 2: Pantheon (Photo: Tony Lewis)

Craig Behenna as Ramal, Tim Morgan as Ari and Andreas Sobik as Ari's Father in the 2006 Oddbodies Theatre Company production in Adelaide. Part 3: Epiphany (Photo: Tony Lewis)

Part 3:

Epiphany

Characters

Actor 1: **Old Roman**, late 60s
Actor 2: **Toby**, 15
Actor 3: **Helen / Zaynab / Ari's Mother**, all early 40s
Actor 4: **Ari's Father / Theatre Technician**, both early 40s
Actor 5: **Stella**, mid 50s
Actor 6: **Mrs Greenberg**, early 60s
Actor 7: **Ari / Young Roman**, both 17
Actor 8: **Saul Greenberg**, 40s **/ Old Man At Airport**, late 60s
Actor 9: **Harry / Uncle Ramal**, both late 30s

Setting

The play takes place:
    Three and a half years since Part 2;
    Two months since Part 1;
    and moves between various locations.

Scene One

The courtyard of Bardwell Detention Centre.
ARI holds a dictaphone.

Ari [*pressing record*] This is Ari. Inmate number 753. Hello, Toby—
my Australian friend. I am standing in the courtyard of Detention
Centre. I can see sky. And stars. And if I stand on my toes, I can
see the wire that cuts. It all around us.

> *Pause.*

I never know that life could change so quickly. In my life, many
change happen. Some bad, some good... And yet I feel lucky.
Perhaps you ask why I should feel so... But I do... I am alive. I am
here.

> *Pause.*

My friend Victor say everyone have story... And it true... He ask me
many time my story. And though I had the words, I could not speak
them. But now I can. Now I tell you my story, Toby. Then you know.

> *The Salat (a Muslim prayer) is heard.*

I come from Kabul. Life there something you don't live. You
survive. Every day like a bad game. Many rules. People, so many
people... disappear. Taken from the streets. From their homes.
There is no play. No sound of laughter. The streets are empty.
Only men with gun...

> *The lights change.*
> *Ari's home in Kabul.*
> *ARI'S MOTHER enters, carrying a baby.*

Mother Where is your father? Stay away from the window.
Ari Perhaps I should go to Uncle Ramal for help?
Mother No.
Ari I can run fast.
Mother Faster than a bullet?

Ari He will come home soon. I know he will.

Mother He has many enemies, your father. He talks too loudly. Defying the Taliban. Secret meetings. I warned him. 'People will find out. The wrong people.' I wish he would stop.

Ari When we are free, then he'll stop. We must believe him. And love him.

Lights reveal ARI'S FATHER, who moans in agony.
He lies upon the floor, RAMAL stands over him.

Father?

Mother What have they done to you? [*To RAMAL*] What happened to him?

Ramal He was tortured... They came to the office and... took him away... But he told them nothing.

Mother Is that all you care about? Protecting others?

Father I'll not name names and cause the deaths of others.

Ari But you will be all right now... won't you?

Silence.

Why don't you look at me?

Father On my arm... under my sleeve...

ARI looks.

What do you see?

Ari Bruising... Puncture marks... What have they done to you?

Ramal He cannot move his legs. In a couple of hours, he will be totally paralysed... A slow-working injection.

Mother No.

Father You must leave me.

Ari No!

Ramal Sssh! Not so loud. Someone might hear you.

Ari No! Please, Father—

Father I don't have much longer, Ari. I don't want you to fight me. Not now. Ramal will help you. I have told him everything.

Mother What? We are to just leave? Leave you? In the dead of night?

Ramal I have passports for you and the children.

Father Ramal will be with you. He will drive you across the border... and make sure you are safe.

Mother How did you get these [*passports*]? How much did you pay for them?

Father All we have. There is no price for freedom.

Ramal Come, we must pack. Quickly. But not too much.

Father Let me see my daughter.

> *MOTHER hands the baby to ARI, who sits near FATHER.*
> *MOTHER and RAMAL exit.*

Don't cry, Ari. You must be strong. For your mother, and for Nasreem. You are the man of the family now.

Ari I hate this country!

Father No. You must never hate this country. It is your home… Once, Ari, Kabul was a beautiful place. A magical city… with colour, and smiling faces… When laughter and music were allowed. One day, when all this is over… when the golden age returns… perhaps you too will return.

Ari I'll never come back. Not if you—

Father I still love my country. So much that I will die for it… I'm sorry, Ari. My mouth always gets me into trouble.

> *MOTHER and RAMAL enter with bags.*
> *FATHER groans in agony.*

Father Take them now, Ramal.

Mother What are we to do without you?

Father Live your life in freedom.

Ari Where?

Father May Allah go with you all. Keep them safe, Ramal.

Ramal I will.

> *MOTHER falls to her knees, over FATHER.*

Mother [*crying*] How can we?

Father No tears. Not now. Save them. For happiness. Go. Ramal— take them—and leave me. Now! Go.

> *ARI drags his MOTHER away. She sobs deeply.*

Remember—you are husband and wife… going on holiday. With your two children… With my children…

The lights change.

ARI is alone.

Ari We drive for long time. We head to border of Pakistan. The road a river full of others. After we cross border, my mother cry. Cry loud like baby. Relief, or sadness… perhaps both. We follow the river of people. On our journey. Towards what? I ask my mother and Uncle Ramal this: 'Towards what?' She say: 'Who knows until we get there'. Here.

Pause.

But she no get here. Or my sister, Nasreem. Or my Uncle Ramal. Only me. This lucky. Strange lucky. Then they capture me and lock me away. And give me a number. And I have too much time to remember. All of us in this place remember too much. And no one want to listen to our stories… So I do as the others do… I close my lips with string and needle. I stop talk. I stop eat. Crazy, yes. For now I have scars inside and outside. As reminder. But it changes nothing… For when I close my eyes… all I see is the water… full of people, floating… like birds…

The lights change.

Scene Two

Anzac Day. Inside Stella's home.

STELLA stares out the window, as TOBY pins medals to HARRY's chest.

Harry What are you looking at, Mum?

Stella The Muslim woman from the flat next door.

Harry When did she move in?

Stella Last week. Haven't seen her husband yet. Someone should tell her to deadhead her geraniums.

Harry You're a fine one to talk. Your garden's like a jungle.

Stella Don't know how they can dress like that in this weather. All covered up. They're taking over.

Harry Mum!

Stella What?!

Harry How many glasses of sherry have you had?

Stella Oh, come on! Don't start picking on me. Not today. I see you every once in a blue moon—at least be nice. I always drink sherry on Anzac Day—the one day of the year—it's a trad—

Harry —a tradition! Yeah, I know. [*He spies a racquet.*] What's with the racquet? You taken up tennis again?

Stella What? No. Just… junk. Cleaning out a few things. You polished your shoes?

Harry Yeah.

Stella Doesn't look like it.

Harry It doesn't matter, does it?

Stella You missed a bit on the side.

Harry Who's going to be looking at my feet?

Stella You can't march on Anzac Day with dirty shoes. It's in memory of your father.

Harry Bet his shoes weren't shiny in Vietnam. Bet they were the last thing he thought about.

Stella Hurry up—or we'll be late.

Toby Here. I'll do it.

> She spits on her handkerchief and hands it to him.

Stella You're a good little boy, Toby. Harry was lucky finding you and your mum. I'll just check the back door.

> STELLA exits.
>
> TOBY cleans HARRY's shoes.

Harry I think she's going mad…

Toby She talks to me like I'm still in kindie.

Stella [*offstage*] You need to do a little wee-wee, Toby?

Toby Um… No thank you.

Harry She's not good with change. It scares her. She's been like that since Dad died.

Toby I think she's lonely. She should get out more. And you haven't told her about tonight.

> STELLA enters.

Stella [*as she comes in*] I'm making a roast for dinner, with the potatoes done just the way you like them. And steamed pudding for dessert. How does that sound?

Harry We can't stay for dinner, Mum.

Stella Beg your pardon?

Harry I've got to work. [*A beat.*] I can't get out of it. Sorry… We can do it another night.

Stella No. It won't be the same.

Harry I'm sorry.

> *Silence.*

Toby Saul Greenberg is giving a talk. You should come.

Stella Thank you, darling, but no thank you.

Toby Here's a flier—if you change your mind.

Harry I'll take you out for dinner next week.

Stella Don't make promises you'll never keep.

> *STELLA moves to door.*

We better get going then. I'll get the bus home after the march.

> *The lights change.*

Scene Three

A room in Bardwell Detention Centre.

HELEN and ARI sit opposite each other across a table, ARI with his dictaphone.

There is an exit sign above the door.

Ari [*into the dictaphone*] Here is first tape for Toby.

Helen He'll be very happy.

Ari I wish I meet him.

Helen I have some good news for you, Ari.

Ari Good news?

Helen We've managed to get you released, on a—

Ari Re-lease? Out of here? I see big exit?

Helen Yes. But—

Ari I come with you now?

Helen No. Not yet. It will take a couple of days, Ari. And it's a temporary protection visa.

Ari Temporary?

Helen Temporary. You understand what that means?

Ari Tem-po-rary?

Helen That means only for a time.

Ari For a time. Then what?

Helen I don't know.

Ari Tem-po-rary... Who take me?

Helen Harry and I are going to take you.

Ari You? And Harry?

Helen Yes.

Ari And Toby?

Helen Yes. And his grandfather, my dad.

Ari I look through Toby's windows at stars! He like me? Toby?

Helen I'm sure he will.

Ari I have new brother. I have Australian brother! Outside. Freedom.
I learn to speak better outside. One day me speak good english.

Helen You'll go to school, with Toby. You'd like that?

Ari Yes. More than any-think. I learn. And then I be in the movie. Up
there... big. Like Mr Bogart... Tem-po-rary...

> *The lights change.*

Scene Four

We hear the GYPSIES singing 'Keserves'.

Inside Helen's home.

OLD ROMAN sits in an armchair.

YOUNG ROMAN enters from the shadows and stands opposite him.

Old Roman I wonder where you are now... If you are... Who you are...
What sort of man you became... If you have lines in your face like
mine... If your bones ache as mine do... Or if you think of me...
as I think of you... as the boy who—I put you on, like a jacket... a
second skin... Do you hope, that one day... by some miracle—?

> *TOBY enters.*
>
> *YOUNG ROMAN disappears.*

Toby Granddad—what are you doing sitting in the dark?

Old Roman I was dreaming.

Toby That's all you do.

Old Roman I'm old!

Toby So you keep telling me.

Old Roman My feet are aching.

> *TOBY sits on the floor, takes OLD ROMAN's shoes off and massages his feet.*

Mmmm… You're a good boy, Toby.

Toby You should be giving me one.

Old Roman How was the march?

Toby Long. But I handed out stacks of fliers.

Old Roman How was Stella?

Toby She was upset about tonight.

Old Roman [*cackling*] I told you! Poor Harry—with a mother like that!

Toby You can't choose your parents. You of all people should know that.

> *Silence.*

You've got to tell Mum.

Old Roman I don't want to talk about it.

Toby When are you going to tell her? She deserves to know—who she really is—who you really are.

Old Roman I'm me. That's who I am.

Toby No, you're not. You're someone else! You're living a lie—

Old Roman Enough!

> *HELEN enters.*

Helen [*as she comes in*] Why is it that every time I walk into a room, the two of you are always arguing? Huh? What's happened between the two of you?

Old Roman Nothing.

Toby Yeah… nothing. You're home early.

Helen Mmm.

Toby Have a good day?

Helen Uh-huh.

Old Roman Did you tell Ari the good news?

Helen Yes. I did. He was very happy. [*To TOBY, producing a tape*] And he gave me this.

She gives it to him.

Toby Excellent!

Helen Listen to it in the car. We've got to meet Saul and his mother at the lecture hall, remember.

Old Roman I'm not coming.

Helen Why not?

Old Roman I'd be in the way.

Helen You would not, Dad.

Old Roman What would I have to say to these people?

Toby A lot.

Helen Their family went through exactly what you did.

Old Roman What do you mean?

Helen The war.

> *Pause.*

Old Roman No. I don't want to go.

Helen [*tired*] Then don't. Do what you want. You shouldn't keep it all bottled up inside. You should talk about it. Before it's too late.

> *HELEN exits.*
>
> *TOBY looks at OLD ROMAN.*

Old Roman What?

Toby You're scared, aren't you? Scared of what she'll think.

> *Silence.*

I know. And I still love you. You're still my granddad.

> *The lights change.*

Scene Five

The lecture hall stage.
SAUL places his papers on a lectern.
A THEATRE TECHNICIAN enters.

Technician Where's ya roadie?

Saul Shopping.

Technician She gunna be much longer?

Saul Possibly.

> *The TECHNICIAN storms off.*
> *SAUL laughs.*
> *Pause.*
> *HARRY, HELEN and TOBY enter.*

Harry Seen any good movies lately?

Saul Aha! I've been counting the days!

Harry Good to see ya.

Saul Yah, ain't it?

Harry Saul, this is Helen—

Saul Aha! The heroic Helen. We finally meet! You're exactly like I imagined.

Helen Really?

Saul Yah. Which is amazing, 'cause I'm usually wrong.

Helen Aw—

Harry And this is Toby. Who has been dying to meet you.

Saul Hello, Toby. I've been dying to meet you, too.

Toby Hello. Am I what you imagined?

Saul No! You're not. You're taller than I expected. And I imagined you with glasses. A blind midget. Completely on the wrong track, huh?

Toby [*laughing*] Uh-huh.

Harry Toby has been handing out fliers all day.

Saul Have you? Thank you! I hope they all come.

Harry And we have some news, about Ari.

Saul Oh, yeah?

Harry [*to HELEN*] You tell him.

Helen Ari is... going to be released.

Saul When?

Harry In a few days, if all goes to plan... A temporary protection visa. We're going to take him. For the time being...

> *SAUL is speechless. He has tears in his eyes.*

You all right, mate?

Saul Yah. Yah. This is good news. [*To TOBY*] And how do you feel about this?

Toby I can't wait. I just hope we like each other.

MRS GREENBERG enters, dressed in Fifth Avenue furs and jewels. Over her right eye she wears an embroidered eye patch. She carries a bag of lemons.

Mrs Greenberg Bingo! It's like a rabbit warren in here. [*To the others*] Hiya!

Toby, Helen & Harry [*together*] Hello...

Saul Helen, Harry, Toby, meet my mother.

Mrs Greenberg Mrs G. But my friends call me Gigi. Like the movie, y'know?

Saul [*nodding at the bag*] Why did you buy so many?

Mrs Greenberg The lady behind the counter was real nice. She was very eager to please. What was I to do?

Saul She was dazzled by your diamonds.

Mrs Greenberg Yah. Or maybe she felt sorry for me 'cause of the patch. Who knows? It's only lemons, anyway. Ugh! These shoes! Are death!

She takes her shoes off.

Saul Mom, please—

Mrs Greenberg My feet are aching!

MRS GREENBERG takes two lemons from the bag, sits down and places them under her feet. She moves her feet back and forth, the lemons massaging her soles. She moans.

God! I need this!

SAUL laughs.

What? They can handle it! They're young and hip!

The TECHNICIAN enters.

Technician Ya back, then?

Mrs Greenberg Yah. Seem so. You want some lemons?

Technician No thanks. Time is money. [*A beat.*] We need to set up your equipment.

Mrs Greenberg I'm onto it. I usually do it all by myself.

Technician [*arrogant*] Ya reckon ya can manage it?

Mrs Greenberg Slide screen and projector. It ain't brain surgery, honey.

Technician Ya have to hang the screen. Reckon ya can handle the ladder?

Mrs Greenberg Sweetie, I walked halfway across Europe when I was twelve. In winter. I think I can handle a ladder.

Technician Right. I'll get you one, then.

The TECHNICIAN exits.

Saul That was very cruel, Mother. He didn't deserve that.

Mrs Greenberg He was giving me attitude! Treating me like an old, one-eyed woman—Don't say a word!

Saul You really going to go up a ladder?

Mrs Greenberg No, *you* are. I hate ladders. You know that. [*With a sigh*] I better go and sweeten him up. With lemons...! Anyone know which way we go?

Helen Yes. It's through here...

HELEN leads the way, followed by HARRY and MRS GREENBERG.

Saul And *that* was my mother!

Toby She's funny!

Saul Yah. She's a riot.

Toby Did she really walk across Europe when she was a child?

Saul Yes. After the war.

Toby Was she in a concentration camp?

Saul Yes. She was.

Toby And when you were a boy, did she talk about it? To you?

Saul Yes. She did. And does. She still tells me things I didn't know. Why do you ask?

Toby My grandfather was in a camp too. But he never talks about it.

Saul Never?

Toby Well, once. To me. His story is different. To what I thought it was. I had no idea. But he hasn't talked about it since. He's too scared to tell Mum. The truth. I don't know what to do.

Saul I see...

Toby Ari made me a tape. He told me his story. The *whole* story. It was awful. And sad. And even though we've never met—I feel as if I *know* him, maybe even better than I know my own granddad. You must think I'm stupid, rambling on—

Saul No. It's good. You must be the kind of guy people like talking to.

Toby Yeah.

Saul I like meeting people who think… about the big things in life. That ain't easy.

Toby Tonight, after your lecture, will you and your mother come back to our house? To meet my granddad.

Saul Deal.

> *HARRY re-enters from one entrance as commotion breaks out on the opposite entrance.*
>
> *STELLA bursts in, having been victorious in a battle with the TECHNICIAN.*

Toby You came.

Harry Mum.

Stella The buses were a nightmare. And the seats were uncomfortable.

Harry Saul, this is Stella, my mother—

Saul Hello—

Stella You've got a nerve—taking my son away from me on Anzac Day.

Harry Mum—

Saul I'm very sorry.

Stella Or perhaps you don't understand how important today is for people in this country.

Harry Mum—please—

Saul Of course I do. That's why—

Stella My husband—his father, fought for this country, to keep it what it is.

Harry White and Christian?

Stella And what's wrong with that? What's wrong with wanting a white Christian country?

Harry Because the world isn't like that any more, Mum. It's changed.

Stella Don't I know it! I'm surrounded by them! Once upon a time you could catch a bus and feel safe.

Harry Mu-um!

Saul Ever read the Bible, Stella?

Stella [*bristling*] I know my way around it.

Saul You pray?

Stella Of course.

Saul I think it was Matthew who said, 'Refugees Mary and Joseph fled Judea to escape violence at the hands of King Herod. They took refuge in Egypt where the local community cared for them.'

Silence.

Jesus Christ and his family weren't blonde, blue-eyed Americans like they are in the movies, you know… they were middle-eastern refugees. Persecuted and on the run. Just like the people you're so afraid of… Perhaps you should try to remember that the next time you pray. It's been very nice meeting you. If you'll excuse me…

SAUL exits.

Harry How dare you do this to me?

Stella I have every right—

Harry No—you don't! You have no right. Not with my friends. Look at you!

Stella What?

Harry Look at what you've become! You never used to be like this. I was so proud of you when I was a kid. You taught me… all of this! You were always looking after people—

Stella If your father was alive—

Harry If Dad was alive, he'd be *here*. 'Cause that's what he believed in. Freedom and peace. *That's* what he fought for.

Stella He'd have hated having them living next door.

Harry No, he wouldn't! He'd have offered to mow their front lawns and had them over for dinner. I don't remember much about him, but I know what he was like.

Silence.

Stella [*in a whisper*] I'm so lonely, Harry.

Harry Then maybe you should make more friends. Have the Muslim woman and her baby over for tea, or sherry, or whatever you drink nowadays. [*Pause.*] We're taking in a refugee, Mum. A boy from Afghanistan. Called Ari. He's going to be a part of our family.

Stella [*stunned*] I didn't know—

Harry Well, now you do. This is my world, Mum. And if you don't like it, then stay away.

HARRY *exits.*

Stella I didn't know.

The lights change.

Scene Six

SAUL addresses the audience.

Saul As long as there have been humans on this planet, there have been wars. And as a result, there have been refugees. Populations move and shift; they always have. And more often than not, they do great things for their new countries.

When I look at the faces of the children I meet on my journeys, I don't just see helpless children. I see evidence of a battle that has gone on since time began. The battle for acceptance.

I have an uncle in New York. He's an unhappy man, grumpy even. Life has not been kind to him—he survived the concentration camp when most of his family didn't. When I was ten, he told me that he believed the problems of the world were due to the fact that 'people don't like other people'. Not deep down, when push comes to shove.

'In survival,' he said, 'one will always think of oneself'.

It horrified me, that thought. Because it made sense... looking back over history... watching the news. Seeing refugees moving into my neighbourhood... 'People don't like other people'... They haunt me, those words. They are why I do what I do. To prove my uncle wrong.

The lights change.

Scene Seven

Stella's home.
STELLA holds the tennis racquet. There is a knock on the door.

Stella Who is it?

Another knock.

79

Who is it?

ZAYNAB enters, holding a baby.

Zaynab I from next door.
Stella What do you want?
Zaynab I sick.
Stella What's wrong with you?
Zaynab Pain. It come, it go. Here— *[appendix]*
Stella Could have been something you've eaten.
Zaynab I need help—
Stella I don't think I can be of much use to you—
Zaynab Please—

STELLA lets her enter.

My name is Zaynab. And this is Zoya.
Stella Stella.
Zaynab Stella. Neighbour. Everybody need good neighbour. I learn that from TV.
Stella Where's your bloke?
Zaynab 'Bloke'?
Stella Your husband. Where is he?
Zaynab In country. He work pick fruit. Send money back. Only work he find. He must take.
Stella What about you and the baby?
Zaynab I look after me. *[Looking at the racquet]* You—tennis?
Stella What? Oh, this. Yes. Once. Long time ago.
Zaynab Latham Hewitt.
Stella Lleyton Hewitt.
Zaynab Lleyton Hewitt. You like him.
Stella Not particularly.
Zaynab Poo I like more. I watch them on TV.
Stella You watch a lot of TV.

ZAYNAB doubles in pain.
STELLA takes the baby.

Zaynab You have baby?
Stella Yes. One. A long time ago. He's all grown-up.
Zaynab You have 'bloke'?

Stella Once. He died. Many years ago.

Zaynab You alone. Like me. We have much in same—

Stella We have much in common.

Zaynab Yes! Just like Bert and Ernie.

> *ZAYNAB doubles in pain.*

I think you take me to hospital now, Stella.

> *The lights change.*

Scene Eight

Toby's house.

TOBY, MRS GREENBERG and SAUL enter, SAUL with a bag of food.

OLD ROMAN is standing.

Old Roman [*to TOBY*] Where's your mother and Harry?

Toby At the Detention Centre. There was a fire. They don't know how long they'll be.

Old Roman Is Ari all right?

Toby I don't know. They said they'll ring, when they find out. [*To the GUESTS*] Please, have a seat.

Old Roman Yes. Please… sit.

Saul Actually, I think I'll head straight to the kitchen. You like spaghetti and meatballs?

Old Roman Yes. I do.

Saul Good.

Toby It's through here.

> *TOBY and SAUL exit.*
>
> *MRS GREENBERG sits on the couch and does her lemon trick.*
>
> *An awkward silence.*

Mrs Greenberg Thanks for having us over.

Old Roman You're welcome. I'm sorry Helen and Harry had to go.

Mrs Greenberg You must be used to it. Being abandoned. I know I am. But I shouldn't complain. Our children do good work, huh?

Old Roman Yes. They do.

Mrs Greenberg There's a whole world of people out there needing help. [*Tapping the couch*] Why don't you siddown?

He does.

There, that's better, isn't it?

Old Roman Yes. Thank you…

Mrs Greenberg So, you got a name? Or do we just call you 'Grandpa'?

Old Roman My name is Roman.

Mrs Greenberg Ha! I got a brother called Roman.

Pause.

Old Roman The lemons—they really work?

Mrs Greenberg Oh, sure. You wanna try…? Go on… I dare you.

OLD ROMAN tries them.

Feels good, huh? Irons out all the lumps.

Old Roman Mmmm… Not bad… My feet… are not what they used to be.

Mrs Greenberg Me too. Mine are always aching. Saul thinks it's because I walked across Europe. After the war.

OLD ROMAN is motionless.

Old Roman So did I.

Mrs Greenberg Really…? Hah… How far did you walk?

Old Roman A long way.

Mrs Greenberg Yah… me too… Where were you?

Silence.

Old Roman Auschwitz. Birkenau.

Mrs Greenberg Me too. [*Pause.*] You were just a child. Like me. [*Tapping her eye patch*] My inheritance.

Silence.

Quite a start to life, huh?

Old Roman Mmmm.

Mrs Greenberg What about your family?

Old Roman I… If… you'll excuse me…

She grabs his arm.

Mrs Greenberg It's okay. I understand. You don't have to tell me. I'm just a nosy old broad… I was luckier, I guess… Some of us were left… We waited for the others for such a long time… hoping… one day there'd be a knock at the door… like in the movies. Or the songs. Miracles… But as you get older you realise that 'Somewhere Over the Rainbow' is just a song—a gorgeous song… but not real life. I'm much better off singing the kinds of songs my grandmother would sing to us. Real life. Warts and all.

Suddenly, MRS GREENBERG starts singing in a croaky voice.

[*Singing*] *Elment a madarka…*
 Üres a kalitka…
 Azt üznte vissza…
 Vissza jö tavaszra…

SAUL and TOBY enter.

Old Roman Someone will return in the springtime…
Mrs Greenberg You know it?
Old Roman If he doesn't return in the spring—he'll come when the grapes are turning soft—if he doesn't return when the grapes are turning soft—
Mrs Greenberg Yah! That's it!
Toby How does it end?
Mrs Greenberg Huh?
Old Roman How does it end?
Mrs Greenberg [*singing*] *Tudd meg soha sem jö.*
Saul You know he will be gone forever.
Old Roman Forever… I…
Mrs Greenberg You know that song?

OLD ROMAN begins to cry.
An awkward silence.

Have I done something to upset you, honey? I'm sorry, sweetie—I should have kept my mouth shut.

OLD ROMAN sobs loudly.
MRS GREENBERG takes his hands and notices his tattoo.

You've got to be joking!
Old Roman What?
Mrs Greenberg B3606…

Old Roman What?

Saul My uncle has the same number tattooed on his arm.

Mrs Greenberg My brother.

Old Roman [*breathless*] His name?

Mrs Greenberg Roman… Kansler.

Toby A gypsy?

Mrs Greenberg Yes.

Old Roman From Hungary.

Mrs Greenberg Yes.

Toby And his uncle—

Saul Ion…

Old Roman And the old woman, who sang…

Mrs Greenberg Viorica… my grandmother…

Old Roman You are—Dora… or Renja?

Mrs Greenberg [*crying*] Renja! Yes…! My God! My God, I know who you are… You're the boy—

Old Roman He's still alive?

Mrs Greenberg Yes. In New York… Just three blocks from my apartment… The boy… Where's my phone?

MRS GREENBERG reaches in her bag and pumps a number into her phone.

Old Roman I thought I would never find him…

Saul He talks about you… still…

Mrs Greenberg [*on her mobile*] Come on… [*It answers.*] Hah! Bingo! Hiya—It's me, your sister… Who else ever rings you up?… Is it?… Sorry!… My clock's all up the putt!… I'm in Adelaide… Adelaide!… Yah. Yah. Saul's as gorgeous as ever… Listen—I've got a surprise for you… No, it ain't chocolates… No—I can't send it. This one's too big to slip into an envelope—

MRS GREENBERG thrusts the mobile to OLD ROMAN, who hesitates before taking it.

Old Roman [*on the mobile*] Hello?… Is that Roman?… It's me… Jan.

The lights change.

Scene Nine

Split scene. Two hospital emergency bays.
In one bay STELLA and ZAYNAB, who is holding Zoya.

Stella You all right?

Zaynab Yes.

Stella Don't know what's keeping them. Here—you've got her all skew whiff. Give her to me.

> *ZAYNAB gives her Zoya.*

There. That's better, isn't it?

Zaynab She like you.

Stella She's a placid little thing, I'll give her that.

Zaynab Before her, I know nothing about babies... where they come from.

Stella Didn't your mother tell you where you came from?

Zaynab Mother died when I just a baby. Live with Grandmother. She tell me she go to market with Mother. And find me on stall with jewel and silk. Mother say, 'What a beau-tiful baby. I want.' Grandmother say, 'Jewel cheaper'. Mother buy me. I her jewel. [*A beat.*] I believe this story... until Zoya come along.

Stella Didn't you learn about things like that at school?

Zaynab In my country no school for girl. Forbidding—

Stella Forbidden.

Zaynab Forbidden. Only for boy.

Stella That's terrible.

Zaynab When girl baby born, no party... no celebration... Boy baby, much fun... big party... firework, gift... everyone happy for boy baby. Zoya... make us happy. We love her very much. She our jewel.

Stella You love them no matter what they are... no matter what.

> *ZAYNAB doubles in pain.*

What's keeping them?

> *The lights change.*
> *ARI sits on a bed in the other bay, his arm bandaged. He talks into the dictaphone.*

Ari Dear Toby. I keep hold of this present. Even in the fire. It survive. Like me. So I still send you my words. I walked toward fire. I no get lost. I know where I go. All I hear is my name called. But I walk away. Get further and further away. Until silence. Can hear nothing. And see nothing. I wait, Toby. For my father and mother. For my sister, to come to me. But they did not come. And the walls explode with fire. And I realise—no one come save me. Only I do that. Up to me. Just like Victor say. A chance. For future. For the memory of my family.

> *The lights change.*
> *STELLA and Zoya.*

Stella [*to Zoya*] Well… just looks like you and me, eh?… You hungry…? Your mum's gone and gotten sick… She'll be all right, though. Yes. She will…. You lovely little thing, with your beautiful big eyes.

> *HARRY enters and sees STELLA. He moves towards her.*
> *TOBY enters behind him.*
> *They watch in silence.*

[*Singing softly*] Pack up all your cares and woes,
> Here I go,
> Singin' low,
> Bye bye, blackbird…

You like that? My boy Harry used to love that song, when he was a baby… But then he grew up… like you will…

Harry I still like the song, though.

> *STELLA turns to him.*

Toby Didn't know you could sing.

Stella Are you two stalking me?

Harry What are you doing here?

Stella Had the neighbour over. Decided to get out more. [*A beat.*] This is Zoya… Zoya, this is Harry… *my* baby… And this is Toby.

> *HARRY places his hand on STELLA's shoulder.*

Harry I love you, Mum.

Stella I know that. I'm not a total idiot.

HARRY laughs.

The lights change.

TOBY moves in the direction of Ari's room. ARI sits up.

Ari Yes?

Toby I'm Toby.

Ari Toby? This is you?

Toby Yes. This is me!

They laugh.

Ari Hello, Toby.

Toby Are you all right?

Ari Yes. More scars. I make new tape for you.

Toby Thanks. We don't really need it any more, do we?

Ari No. [*Pause.*] So, when I come home… what will we do?

Toby Lots of things… whatever you want. We can… listen to music… play on the computer… make movies.

Ari You can do this? Make movie?

Toby Sure.

Ari Wow! Make movie. What else we do?

Toby Go to the beach for a swim, read, eat, go for a skate in the park.

Ari Skate? What is skate?

Toby You have wheels. On your feet.

TOBY demonstrates in mime.

Ari Ah—skate! Yes. I like the sound of it. Skate… skate. What else?

Toby I dunno… just… hang out… I guess.

Ari [*perplexed*] 'Hang out'? On what do we hang?

Toby No. I mean… just… we'll just… do stuff together… you and me… 'hang out'.

Ari 'Hang out'. Yes. That's nice… Hang out.

The lights change.

Scene Ten

TOBY addresses the audience.

Toby [*to the audience*] That night, when we went home, Granddad told Mum everything—told her the whole story—how he'd

87

changed his name—how he'd walked away from his own family—how he'd lived a lie—all because of his shame, and the memory of a boy he once knew. She didn't get angry. She listened to everything he said. And afterwards, she cried. Not because of the lies, or the shock, but because she lived her whole life with this man, her *father*, and didn't know.

> *'Au Fond du Temple Sant' is heard.*
>
> *The lights change.*
>
> *Two weeks later. Inside an airport arrivals lounge.*
>
> *OLD ROMAN stands waiting.*
>
> *An elderly man with a suitcase enters from a distance away.*
>
> *The two old men catch sight of each other, and draw closer. They roll up their sleeves and show their tattoos. They embrace.*
>
> *The lights change.*

Scene Eleven

Stella's overgrown, moonlit garden. A path of light spirals to a bench centre stage.

ARI enters, followed by TOBY, filming.

Ari You still film me?

Toby Of course. That's all I've been doing for three weeks now.

Ari Follow me—as I lead you to the Lost Ark!

> *He screams, writhing in mock terror.*

Ugh! Spiders!

> *TOBY laughs.*

Toby You're crazy.

Ari No! I'm Halison Ford. And you are Spillburger.

Toby Spiel-berg. Spielberg.

Ari Yeah, him too. Okay! Follow!

> *They run to the bench as ZAYNAB, with Zoya, follows STELLA through the garden.*

Stella It's too overgrown. Needs cutting back.

Zaynab No! It is beautiful. An oasis. I want a garden just like this. For Zoya.

Stella She'd go missing. We'd have to send out a search party.

Zaynab You can lead it—hack through the jungle with your tennis racquet.

STELLA laughs and waves her stick around.

ZAYNAB laughs also.

HARRY enters followed by SAUL.

Harry Just follow me…

Saul It's like the Garden of Eden!

Harry Ya reckon?

Saul Anyone seen my mother? Tall woman with high heels and one eye?

Mrs Greenberg [*offstage*] I heard that!

Laughter.

Saul Where are you?

Mrs Greenberg [*offstage*] I have *no* idea…

Harry Are you all right?

MRS GREENBERG stumbles from the shadows, clutching lemons.

Mrs Greenberg Bingo! Found the lemon tree!

Saul You've been gone for ages… Why are you walking like that?

Mrs Greenberg I broke my heel. Very expensive shoes. But it was worth it.

She kicks off her heels and proceeds with a lemon massage.

ARI laughs.

Ugh! I adore this country!

Harry Ready for some fireworks?

Stella Oooh, yes!

Harry Shall we?

Saul Uh-huh—you lead the way.

They exit.

Ari Firework for Zoya.

Stella Yes. And for you too.

Ari It's not my birthday.

Stella Doesn't matter. What's this [*a flower*]?

Ari Flower.

Stella *Hibiscus. Rosa sinensis.*

Ari *Rosa sin-en-sis*... So many beautiful words...

> *ARI offers it to her, and she takes it.*
>
> *The fireworks begin.*
>
> *Everyone turns their eyes to the sky, the colours flashing across their faces.*
>
> *The lights fade out.*

END OF PART THREE

Lightning Source UK Ltd.
Milton Keynes UK
UKOW07f0954261114

242204UK00001B/14/P